Scottish Family History on the Web

A DIRECTORY

Third Edition

G000082530

Stuart A. Raymond

THE FAMILY HISTORY PARTNERSHIP

Published by
The Family History Partnership
PO Box 502
Bury BL8 9EP

in association with
S.A. & M.J Raymond

Email: samjraymond@btopenworld.com
Website: **www.stuartraymond.co.uk**

ISBNs
Family History Partnership: 978 1 906280 21 5
S.A. & M.J. Raymond: 978 1 899668 60 1

Third edition 2010

The previous editions of this book
were published by the
Federation of Family History Societies
in 2002 and 2005

Printed and bound by Information Press
Southfield Road, Eynsham
Oxford OX29 4JB

Contents

Introduction

A vast amount of information concerning genealogy and family history is now available on the internet. Surfing the net can be a very productive process for the researcher; it can, however, also be very frustrating. Despite the fact that there are thousands of genealogical web sites worth visiting, the means for finding particular relevant sites are very poor: search engines frequently list dozens of irrelevant sites, but not the ones you require. This book is intended to help you identify those sites which are most likely to be relevant to your research. The listing is selective; I have only included those sites which are of general interest to most genealogists. Consequently, I have excluded sites devoted solely to particular families. The innumerable sites which are, in theory, international in scope, but in practice are primarily of interest to American genealogists, are also excluded, as are those sites which are of general, rather than specifically genealogical interest, e.g. general search engines, commercial sites such as Amazon, etc. Many of the sites which I have listed, especially those in chapters 1, 7, and 8, can be used to find these excluded categories.

It should be noted that **http://** should be prefixed to all URLs listed in this directory.

This listing is as up to date as I have been able to make it. However, new web pages are being mounted all the time, and URLs frequently change. Consequently, it is anticipated that this directory will need frequent updating. If you are unable to find a site listed here, then you should check Cyndis List or one of the other gateways listed in chapter 1 below; the probability is that the site has moved to another address. Alternatively, search words from the title - or the URL - on a search engine such as **www.google.com**. If a website has been removed from its server, it is likely that a copy has been archived at **www.archive.org**, where it can be read. If you know of sites which have not been included here, please let me know so that they can be included in the next edition of this directory.

My thanks go to Bob Boyd, who has seen this edition through the press, and to my partners in the Family History Partnership for their continued support.

Stuart A. Raymond

1. Gateways, Search Engines, *etc.*

There are a variety of gateways and search engines for Scottish genealogists. Cyndis list is the major international gateway, with a lengthy listing of Scottish websites. Genuki provides both extensive introductory information and links to innumerable sites. Quite a number of other sites offer similar help. General search engines are not listed here: they may be found on Cyndis List.

- Cyndis List: Scotland
  www.CyndisList.com/scotland.htm
- Genuki: Scotland
  www.genuki.org.uk/big/sct
- Scotland: Genealogy
  www.genuki.org.uk/big/sct/Genealogy.html
  Links and bibliography
- The Scotland Gen Web Project
  www.scotlandgenweb.org
- UK Genealogy: Scottish Research
  www.ukgenealogy.co.uk/scotland.htm
- Genealogylinks.net
  www.genealogylinks.net/uk/scotland/index.html
  Gateway
- Genealogy of the UK: Scotland Genealogy
  www.genealogy-of-uk.com/Scotland/index.html
  Links pages for every county
- Linkpendium: Scotland
  http://genealogy-uki.linkpendium.com/scot/
- Rampant Scotland Directory: Genealogy
  www.rampantscotland.com
  Gateway
- Epodunk UK Communities List: Scotland
  http://uk.epodunk.com/communities-scotland.html
  Links to sites for particular places. For particular counties, visit
  /historic-counties-scotland.html

- Scotlands Family
  www.scotlandsfamily.com
- Scottish and LDS Genealogical Reference Information
  www.ktb.net/~dwills/scotref/13300-scottishreference.htm
  Brief introductory information with links to a few important web-sites
- Scottish Genealogy Research Source Directory
  http://thecapitalscot.com/scotgenealogy/home.html
- Scottish Web Sites
  http://homepages.ihug.co.nz/~origins/scotland.htm
- Tracing your Scottish Ancestry
  www.geo.ed.ac.uk/home/scotland/genealogy.html
  Brief gateway
- Viv Dunstan's Indexes
  www.vivdunstan.co.uk/indexes/index.html
  Notes on various indexes under compilation or planned for publication.

2. General introductions to Scottish Genealogy & History

Genuki (see chapter 1) is probably the most comprehensive introductory site currently available. Family Search's Research Wiki is also useful, and perhaps more authoritative. There are numerous other introductory sites for the Scottish genealogist. Some of these are listed here - although many of the other sites listed elsewhere in this directory also have useful introductory information.

- Ancestral Scotland
  www.ancestralscotland.com
  Genealogy site from the Scottish Tourist Board
- BIFHS-USA Guide to British Isles Research, V: Scotland
  www.rootsweb.ancestry.com/~bifhsusa/ressco.html#scotland
- Family History
  www.scan.org.uk/familyhistory
  From the Scottish Archive Network
- Family History: an introduction to Scottish Family History
  www.nls.uk/family-history/index.html
  From the National Library of Scotland
- Family Search Research Wiki
  https://wiki.familysearch.org/en/Portal%3AScotland
- Scottish Genealogical Services: Genealogical Resources and Hints
  www.kinhelp.co.uk/KinHelp/genealogical-resources-hints
- Introduction to Scottish Family History
  www.genuki.org.uk/big/sct/intro.html
- Rootsweb Guide to Tracing Family Trees: Irish, Scot-Irish, Scottish
  www.rootsweb.com/~rwguide/lesson21.htm

- Scotlands People: Getting Started
  www.scotlandspeople.gov.uk/content/help/index.aspx?r=1
- Scottish Family History Research and Advice
  www.electricscotland.com/webclans/scotroot.htm
- Tracing Your Scottish Ancestry
  www.geo.ed.ac.uk/home/Scotland/genealogy.html
  Introduction
- Scottish Roots
  www.bbc.co.uk/scotland/history/scottishroots
  From the BBC
- Searching Scottish Family History from Canada
  www.bifhsgo.ca/classics/john_hay_scottish_family_history.pdf

For the wider picture, it may be useful to check sites of general historical interest. Visit:
- Cameron's Gateway to Scottish History
  http://cunninghamc.tripod.com/Homepage12_97/index.htm
- Gazetteer for Scotland History Time-line
  www.geo.ed.ac.uk/scotgaz/timeline.html
- Scotland: History
  www.genuki.org.uk/big/sct/History.html
- Scottish History Online
  www.north-scotland.co.uk
- SCRAN
  www.scran.ac.uk
  Scottish history and culture
- Scotlands Pages: Scotlands Written History
  www.nls.uk/scotlandspages/index.html
  Includes time-line; from the National Library of Scotland
- Scottish Event & Historical Timeline
  http://hometown.aol.com/Skylander/timeline.html
- A Timeline of Scottish History
  www.rampantscotland.com/timeline/timeline.htm
- Timeline of Scottish History: Undiscovered Scotland
  www.undiscoveredscotland.co.uk/usfeatures/timeline/index.html

3. Libraries, Record Offices & Books

Most of the information sought by genealogists can be found in books and archival sources. The libraries and record offices which hold these resources provide an essential genealogical service, which should not be neglected. Most have websites (including online catalogues), which are listed here. For the libraries of family history societies, consult the websites listed in chapter 4.

It is impossible in the compass of this book to provide a complete list of library and record office web sites likely to be of use to Scottish genealogists. Such a list would have to include most public and university libraries, and is outside the scope of this book. However, a number of sites provide general listings. See:

- Scotland: Archives and Libraries
  www.genuki.org.uk/big/sct/Archives.html
- BUBL UK: Libraries
  www.bubl.ac.uk/uk/bubluklibraries.htm
  Directory of UK national, public and university libraries
- Libdex
  www.libdex.com
  Directory of libraries world-wide
- Scottish Library and Information Resources
  http://scone.strath.ac.uk/slir/index.cfm
- The UK Public Libraries: Public Libraries on the Web
  http://dspace.dial.pipex.com/town/square/ac940/ukpublib.html
  Lists public libraries on the Web, with details of services

Two union catalogues of books are available:
- Copac National, Academic and Specialist Library Caztalogue
  www.copac.ac.uk
  Union catalogue of UK and Irish national and university libraries, including several major Scottish institutions
- CAIRNS: Co-operative Information Retrieval Network for Scotland
  http://cairns.lib.strath.ac.uk

For archive repositories, see:
- Scottish Archive Network
  www.scan.org.uk
  Includes a directory of repositories, and much general information
- Scottish Record Offices and Archives on the Web
  www.oz.net/~markhow/scotsros.htm
- Records Office Finder: Scotland
  www.mytimemachine.co.uk/scottisharchives.htm
- Archon Directory
  www.nationalarchives.gov.uk/archon
  Directory of archive repositories throughout the UK
- Research Collections Online
  http://scone.strath.ac.uk/rco/RCOService/ColnSel.cfm
- The National Register of Archives for Scotland
  www.nas.gov.uk/nras
  For a general introduction to Scottish libraries and record offices, visit:
- Family Search Research Wiki: Scotland Archives and Libraries
  https://wiki.familysearch.org/en/Scotland_Archives_and_Libraries

Major Institutions

Scotlands People Centre
- Scotlands People Centre
  www.scotlandspeoplehub.gov.uk

National Archives of Scotland
- National Archives of Scotland
  www.nas.gov.uk

- Records in the National Archives of Scotland / Diane Baptie
  http://genealogypro.com/articles/NAS.html
  General discussion

National Library of Scotland
- National Library of Scotland
  www.nls.uk

The National Archives
- The National Archives
  www.nationalarchives.gov.uk
  The major British archives repository. Gives access to an extensive catalogue, and much, much more!

British Library
- British Library
  www.bl.uk
- British Library Catalogues on the Web
  http://blpc.bl.uk/reshelp/findhelprestype/catblhold/all/allcat.html
  Includes catalogues of books, manuscripts, newspapers, maps, journals, *etc*.

Family History Library
- Family History Library
  www.familysearch.org
  Library of the Latter Day Saints; extensive site with numerous pages. Includes a list of Family History Centres in Scotland

University Libraries
- The Scottish Universities: their libraries and archives
  members.ozemail.com.au/~jimjar/jimjargg.htm
  Guide for the genealogist
- University of Aberdeen: Historic Collections
  www.abdn.ac.uk/diss/historic
  Extensive archives from the University and the locality
- University of Dundee Archive Services
  www.dundee.ac.uk/archives
  The archives include the Brechin Diocesan archives, and many records of public and commercial organisations, estates, *etc*.

- The University of Edinburgh Special Collections
  www.lib.ed.ac.uk/resources/collections/specdivision
- Heriot-Watt University, Edinburgh: Archive, Records Management and Museum Service
  www.hw.ac.uk/archive
  Includes details of business, estate, and educational records held.
- University of Glasgow Archive Services
  www.gla.ac.uk/archives
- St. Andrews University Library Special Collections
  www.st-andrews.ac.uk/specialcollections
  Includes burgh, kirk sessions, estate, and business records of Fife, *etc*.
- University of Strathclyde Archives
  www.strath.ac.uk/archives

Museums
- National Museums of Scotland
  www.nms.ac.uk
  Click on `Collections & Research', `Social & Technological History', then either `Armed Forces History' or `Scottish Life Archive' for details of various collections in Scottish museums
- Glasgow Museums
  www.glasgowmuseums.com

Other Institutions
- Scottish Records Association
  www.scottishrecordsassociation.org
- The Stair Society
  www.stairsociety.org/home.htm
  Publishers of legal records which may be of use to family historians

Aberdeenshire
- Aberdeenshire Archives and Libraries
  www.urie.demon.co.uk/genuki/ABD/archives.html
  Overview
- Aberdeen City Archives
  www.aberdeencity.gov.uk/LocalHistory/archives/loc_ArchivesHomePage.asp

- Aberdeen City Council: Local Studies
  www.aberdeencity.gov.uk/Libraries/lib/Lib_LocalStudies.asp

Angus
- Angus Archives and Libraries
  www.genuki.org.uk/big/sct/ANS/Archives
  Overview
- Angus Archives
  www.angus.gov.uk/history/archives
- Angus Council: Libraries
  www.angus.gov.uk/history/libraries/default.htm
  Details of local history resources at Arbroath, Brechin, Carnoustie, Forfar, Kirriemuir, Montrose, & Monifieth
- Dundee City Council: Archives
  www.dundeecity.gov.uk/archives
- Dundee City Library Local History Centre
  www.dundeecity.gov.uk/centlib/loc_stud.htm
- Friends of Dundee City Archives
  www.fdca.org.uk
  Includes databases
- The Lamb Collection
  www.dundeecity.gov.uk/lamb/main.htm
  Major local history collection held by Dundee Central Library

Argyll
- Argyll & Bute Council: Local History Information
  www.argyll-bute.gov.uk/content/education/libraries/
  localhistory/localstudies
  Includes pages on the Council's Archives and Local Studies Departments

Ayrshire
- Ayrshire Archives and Libraries
  www.genuki.org.uk/big/sct/AYR/archive.html
  Overview
- Ayrshire Roots genealogy
  http://fp.ayrshireroots.plus.com/Genealogy/Records/
  Archives/Archives.htm
  Details of archive repositories and libraries for Ayrshire

- Ayrshire Archives
  www.ayrshirearchives.org.uk
- The Scottish & Local History Library
  www.rootsweb.com/~sctayr/southayr.html
  Resources at Ayr Library
- South Ayrshire Libraries: Local History
  www.south-ayrshire.gov.uk/libraries/local-history.aspx
- East Ayrshire Library Service
  www.rootsweb.com/~sctayr/eastayr.html
  List of resources
- [Ardrossan Local History Unit]
  www.rootsweb.com/~sctayr/northayr.html
  List of resources
- Maybole Historical Society's Local and Family History Centre
  www.maybole.org/community/organisations/historical/centre.htm

Berwickshire
See Roxburghshire

Buteshire
See also Argyll
- Isle of Arran Heritage Museum
  www.arranmuseum.co.uk
  Includes a 'Genealogy Section' and an 'Archives Section'

Caithness
- The North Highland Archive
  www.highland.gov.uk/leisureandtourism/
  what-to-see/archives/northhighlandarchives
  Covers Caithness, Sutherland, Ross & Cromarty, Invernessshire, and Nairnshire

Clackmannanshire
- Clackmannanshire Archives
  www.clacksweb.org.uk/culture/archives
- Clacksweb: Local History & Local Studies Service
  www.clacksweb.org.uk/culture/localhistoryandlocalstudies

Dumfriesshire
- Dumfries & Galloway: Local Studies, Archives & Family History
  www.dumgal.gov.uk/index.aspx?articleid=2297

Dunbartonshire
- Dunbartonshire Libraries
  www.scotlandgenweb.org/dunbartonshire/libraries.html
- East Dunbartonshire Council: Family History/Local Studies
  www.eastdunbarton.gov.uk
  Click `learning', `library information services', and `family
  history' or `local studies'. Details of library resources.
- West Dunbartonshire Libraries: Local Studies and Archives
  http://libraryonline.west-dunbarton.gov.uk/
  rooms/portal/page/70_Local_Studies_and_Archives

East Lothian
- East Lothian Council: Local History Centre
  www.eastlothian.gov.uk/site/scripts/
  documents_info.php?documentID=369
- East Lothian Archive Service
  www.eastlothian.gov.uk/site/scripts/documents_info.php?
  categoryID=428&documentID=534

Fife
- Fife Direct A-Z: Archives
  www.fifedirect.org.uk/atoz
  Search 'Archives'
- Fife Council Archive Centre
  www.genuki.org.uk/big/sct/FIF/libraries/Archives.htm
  Lists main holdings, with separate pages for parochial board/
  parish council records, school records, burgh and town
  council records, and various places.
- Cupar Library
  www.genuki.org.uk/big/sct/FIF/libraries/Cupar_lib.htm
- Dunfermline Carnegie Library
  www.genuki.org.uk:8080/big/sct/FIF/libraries/Dunfermline_lib.htm
- Kirkcaldy Central Library
  www.genuki.org.uk/big/sct/FIF/libraries/Kirkcaldy_lib.htm

- Methil Library
  www.genuki.org.uk/big/sct/FIF/libraries/Methil_lib.htm
- St. Andrews Library
  www.genuki.org.uk:8080/big/sct/FIF/libraries/StAndrews_lib.htm
- Hay Fleming Reference Library
  www.st-andrews.ac.uk/specialcollections/Rarebooks/
  Namedspecialcollections/HayFlemingCollection
  Collection for St. Andrews, now held by the University

Invernessshire
See also Caithness
- The Highland Archive and Registration Centre
  www.highland.gov.uk/leisureandtourism/what-to-see/
  archives/highlandcouncilarchives
  Includes the Highland Council Genealogy Centre
- Clan Donald Centre: Library and Study Centre
  www.clandonald.com/index.php/page/library
  Library for Skye, the Western Isles and the West Highlands, run by the
  Clan Donald Lands Trust

- Lochaber Archive Centre
  www.highland.gov.uk/leisureandtourism/what-to-see/
  archives/lochaberarchives

- Seallam! Visitor Centre
  www.seallam.com/intro.htm
  For Harris and the Western Isles

Kinrossshire
See also Perthshire
- Kinross Museum
  www.kinrossmuseum.co.uk

Lanarkshire
- The Mitchell
  www.glasgow.gov.uk/en/Residents/Library_Services/The_Mitchell
- Virtual Mitchell: Images of Glasgow
  www.mitchelllibrary.org/virtualmitchell/index.php

- Bellshill Family History Centre
  www.northlanarkshire.gov.uk/index.aspx?articleid=16514
- Motherwell Heritage Centre
  www.monklands.co.uk/leisure/motherwellher.htm
- Strathclyde Area Genealogy Centre
  www.glasgow.gov.uk/en/Residents/BirthDeathMarriage_
  Citizenship/GenealogyCentre
- South Lanarkshire Council: Records & Archives
  www.southlanarkshire.gov.uk
  Search 'Archives'

Midlothian
- Edinburgh City Archives
  www.edinburgh.gov.uk/internet/Council/Council_Business/
  CEC_edinburgh_city_archives_2
- Exploring Edinburgh: Edinburgh Room
  www.edinburgh.gov.uk/internet/Leisure/Libraries/Explore_
  your_library/Exploring_Edinburgh/CEC_exploring_
  edinburgh__the_edinburgh_room
- Midlothian: Local Studies Homepage
  www.midlothian.gov.uk//Article.aspx?TopicId=0&ArticleId=16877
- Midlothian District Library: Local Studies Centre
  www.genuki.org.uk:8080/big/sct/MLN/LocalStudies.html
- Do You Have Any Scottish Ancestry?
  www.ancestor.abel.co.uk/index.html
  Primarily concerned with Midlothian, especially Duddingston,
  Inveresk, Liberton and Newton. Many extracts from original
  sources

Moray
- Local Heritage Services in Moray
  www.moray.gov.uk/LocalHeritage

Nairnshire
See Caithness

Orkney
- The Orkney Library and Archive
  www.orkneylibrary.org.uk
  Official site

- The Orkney Library and Archives
  www.genuki.org.uk/big/sct/OKI/archives.html

Peebleshire
See Roxburghshire

Perthshire
- Perthshire: Local and Family History Service
  www.pkc.gov.uk/Education+and+learning/Libraries+
  archives+and+learning+centres/Libraries+local+and+
  special+collections
  In the A.K.Bell Library
- Perth and Kinross Council Archives
  www.pkc.gov.uk/Education+and+learning/Libraries+archives+and+
  learning+centres/Archives/Perth+and+Kinross+Council+Archive.htm

Renfrewshire
- Inverclyde Council: Local and Family History
  www.inverclyde.gov.uk/Category.aspx?catid=1792

Ross & Cromarty
See Caithness

Roxburghshire
- Heritage Hub: Scottish Borders Archive and Local History Centre
  www.heartofhawick.co.uk/heritagehub
  www.scotborders.gov.uk/council/specialinterest/
  heartofhawick/18964.html
  Covers Berwickshire, Peeblesshire, Roxburghshire, & Selkirkshire

Selkirkshire
See Roxburghshire

Shetland
- Shetland Islands Council: Archives
  www.shetland.gov.uk/archives
  Very brief
- Shetland Museum & Archives
  www.shetlandmuseumandarchives.org.uk/

Stirlingshire

- Falkirk Council Archives
  **www.falkirk.gov.uk/services/community/cultural_services/
  museums/a rchives/archive.aspx**
- Stirling Council: Archives
  www.stirling.gov.uk/index/accessinformation/archives.htm
- Stirling Council: Family History
  www.stirling.gov.uk/index/services/libraries/family_history.htm
  Includes page on local history, which has 'People Indexes' for
  1911-1939 & 1940-69

Sutherland
See Caithness & Invernessshire

West Lothian
- West Lothian Council Archives
  www.westlothian.gov.uk/tourism/libservices/ves
- West Lothian Council: Local History Library
  **www.westlothian.gov.uk/tourism/libservices/LocSpec/
  LocalHistoryLibrary**

Wigtownshire
See Dumfries

Books
It cannot be emphasized too strongly that books continue to be vital to
genealogical research. Record publications are particularly important, and
are described in:
- National Archives of Scotland: Published Guides and Sources
  www.nas.gov.uk/guides/publishedSources.asp

Bibliographies listing books relevant to family history are essential reference works. The Scottish genealogist is fortunate that a number are available on the internet.
- Scottish Bibliographies Online
  www.scotlandsculture.org/sbo/sbo.htm

- A selected bibliography for Scottish Research in the N.Y.G. &
  B. Library
  www.newyorkfamilyhistory.org
  Click on `research aids', `bibliographies', and title. Based on the
  holdings of New York Genealogical & Biographical Society
  (now in New York Public Library), but of value to all
  researchers
- Sources for Research in Scottish Genealogy
  www.loc.gov/rr/genealogy/bib_guid/scotland.html
  Valuable bibliography from the Library of Congress
- Sources for Scottish and Scots-American Genealogy
  http://wilson.lib.umn.edu/reference/sco-gene.html
  Bibliography
- Scottish Texts and Calendars: an analytical guide to serial publications /
  David & Wendy B. Stevenson
  www.nls.uk/print/search/preface.pdf
  Bibliography of record society publications, including publications of
  Scottish organizations, some of which are vital for genealogists. This is
  a digitised image of a published book. It is updated by:
- Royal Historical Society Bibliography: Guide to Record
  Societies and their Publications
  www.rhs.ac.uk/bibl/docs/histsocs.html

The genealogical library of John A. Robertson is listed here:
- Some Scottish books
  www.ancestor.abel.co.uk/books.html

Aberdeenshire
- Aberdeenshire Bibliography
  www.urie.demon.co.uk/genuki/ABD/bibliography.html

Angus
- Bibliography of Angus
  www.angus.gov.uk/history/archives/resources/bibliography.htm

Ayrshire
- Ayrshire Bibliography
  www.ayrshirehistory.org.uk/Bibliography/books_intro.htm

Kinrossshire
- Kinross Bibliography
  www.kinrossmuseum.co.uk/bibliography.htm

Orkney
- Bibliography of Orkney Family Genealogies
  www.genuki.org.uk/big/sct/OKI/BibFamGen.html
- Books relating to the history of the Orkney Islands
  www.genuki.org.uk/big/sct/OKI/history.html

4. Family History Societies

Most Scottish family history societies have web-sites. These generally provide information on the society - names of officers, meetings, membership information, publications, services offered, lists of members interests, *etc.* Full lists of societies are available at:

- Family History and Genealogy Societies: Scotland
  www.genuki.org.uk/Societies/Scotland.html
- UK Genealogy Local Societies
  www.ukgenealogy.co.uk/societies.htm
- Scottish Association of Family History Societies: Membership
  www.safhs.org.uk/SAFHS_Members.asp

Reference may also be made to the list of societies in:
- Cyndis List: Scotland
  www.cyndislist.com/scotland.htm

National Societies
- Scottish Association of Family History Societies
  www.safhs.org.uk
  The 'surname search' function indexes all the websites of member societies
- Scottish Genealogy Society
  www.scotsgenealogy.com
- Society of Genealogists
  www.sog.org.uk
  There is a separate page listing Scottish resources at
  /prc/sct.shtml
- Anglo-Scottish Family History Society
  www.mlfhs.org.uk
  Click name. A branch of the Manchester & Lancashire Family History Society

- The Guild of One-Name Studies
  www.one-name.org
- The Heraldry Society of Scotland
  www.heraldry-scotland.co.uk

Overseas Societies

Australia
- Heraldry & Genealogy Society of Canberra, Inc: Scottish S.I.G.
  www.hagsoc.org.au
- Scottish Group, Genealogical Society of Queensland
  www.gsq.org.au/society/scottish.html
  Click on `Activities' & 'SIG's'
- South Australian Genealogy & Heraldry Society, Inc: Scottish Group
  www.saghs.org.au/sctgroup.htm
- Scottish Ancestry Group: a service group of the Genealogical Society of Victoria
  www.gsv.org.au/activities/groups/sag
- Western Australian Genealogical Society, Inc. Special Interest Group. Scottish
  www.wags.org.au/groups/sigscot.htm
  Click 'Special Interest Groups'

Canada
- British Isles Family History Society of Greater Ottowa
  www.bifhsgo.ca

New Zealand
- New Zealand Society of Genealogists Scottish Interest Group
  www.genealogy.org.nz/Scottish_Interest_Group_210.aspx

United States
- British Isles Family History Society, USA: Scottish Study Group
  www.rootsweb.ancestry.com/~bifhsusa/study-scottish.html

County and Local Societies

Aberdeenshire
- Aberdeen & North-East Scotland Family History Society
  www.anesfhs.org.uk
  Covers Aberdeenshire, Banffshire, Kincardineshire, & Moray

- The Family History Society of Buchan
  www.fhsb.org.uk

Angus
See Perthshire

Argyll
See Caithness & Lanarkshire

Ayrshire
- Alloway & Southern Ayrshire Family History Society
  www.maybole.org/history/resources/asafhs.htm
- East Ayrshire Family History Society
  www.eastayrshirefhs.org.uk
- Largs & North Ayrshire Family History Society
  www.largsnafhs.org.uk
- Troon & Ayrshire Family History Society
  www.troonayrshirefhs.org.uk

Banffshire
See Aberdeenshire

Berwickshire
- Borders Family History Society
  www.bordersfhs.org.uk
  Covers Berwickshire, Peeblesshire, Roxburghshire, & Selkirkshire

Buteshire
See Lanarkshire

Caithness
- Caithness Family History Society
  www.caithnessfhs.org.uk
- The Highland Family History Society
  www.highlandfhs.org.uk
  Covers Caithness, Sutherland, Ross & Cromarty, Invernessshire, Nairnshire, and parts of northern Argyll

Clackmannanshire
- Central Scotland Family History Society
  www.csfhs.org.uk
  Covers Clackmannanshire, West Perthshire, Stirlingshire, & parts of West Lothian

Dumfriesshire
- Dumfries and Galloway Family History Society
  www.dgfhs.org.uk

Dunbartonshire
See Lanarkshire

East Lothian
See Midlothian

Fife
See also Perthshire
- Fife Family History Society
  www.fifefhs.org

Invernessshire
See Caithness

Kincardineshire
See Aberdeenshire

Kinrossshire
See Perthshire

Kirkcudbrightshire
See Dumfriesshire

Lanarkshire
- Glasgow & West of Scotland Family History Society
  www.gwsfhs.org.uk
  Covers Argyll, Buteshire, Ayrshire, Dunbartonshire, Lanarkshire, Renfrewshire & part of Stirlingshire

- Lanarkshire Family History Society
  www.lanarkshirefhs.org.uk

Midlothian
- The Lothians Family History Society
  www.lothiansfhs.org.uk
  Covers East Lothian, Midlothian, & West Lothian

Moray
See also Aberdeenshire
- Moray & Nairn Family History Society
  www.morayandnairnfhs.co.uk

Nairnshire
See Caithness, & Moray

Orkney
- Sib Folk: the Website of the Orkney Family History Society
  www.orkneyfhs.co.uk

Peeblesshire
See Berwickshire & Roxburghshire

Perthshire
See also Clackmannanshire
- North Perthshire Family History Group
  www.npfhg.org
- Tay Valley Family History Society
  www.tayvalleyfhs.org.uk

Renfrewshire
See also Lanarkshire
- Renfrewshire Family History Society
  www.renfrewshirefhs.co.uk

Ross & Cromarty
See Caithness

Roxburghshire
See Berwickshire

Selkirkshire
See Berwickshire

Shetland
- Shetland Family History Society
  www.shetland-fhs.org.uk

Stirlingshire
See Clackmannanshire

Sutherland
See Caithness

West Lothian
See also Clackmannanshire and Midlothian
- West Lothian Family History Society
  www.wlfhs.org.uk

Wigtownshire
See Dumfriesshire

5. Discussion Groups

Want to ask someone who knows? Then join an online discussion group or forum. For general information on these, visit:
- Mailing Lists: What are they?
  helpdesk.rootsweb.com/help/mail1.html

Mailing lists historically required you to subscribe (i.e. register). Some groups still require subscription, but others you can use without registering. Payment is not usually required.

There are far too many groups to list them all here. Some are general; others are devoted to topics such as the Highland Clearances or Tombstone inscriptions. The majority cover research in particular counties or areas. Some of these are hosted by family history societies, whose websites are listed in chapter 4. In order to identify others, the best place to begin is John Fuller's

- Genealogy Resources on the Internet: Scotland Mailing Lists
  www.rootsweb.ancestry.com/~jfuller/gen_mail_country-unk-sct.html

See also:
- Genealogy Mailing Lists
  www.genuki.org.uk/indexes/MailingLists.html
- Cyndis List: Mailing Lists
  www.CyndisList.com/mailing.htm

Many mailing lists are hosted by Rootsweb. They are listed at
- Rootsweb: Mailing Lists
  http://lists.rootsweb.ancestry.com/index/index.html

To search Rootsweb mailing list archives, visit:
- Archives Search Engine
  http://archiver.rootsweb.ancestry.com/cgi-bin/search

Many groups are hosted at:
- Google Groups
  http://groups.google.com
  For relevant groups, search `Genealogy'

Others can be searched for at:
- Yahoo Groups
  http://groups.yahoo.com

A variety of forums are hosted at:
- Talking Scot
  www.talkingscot.com/forum

A number of sites are devoted solely to county mailing lists. These include:
- Ancestry.com Message Boards: Scotland
  http://boards.ancestry.com/localities.britisles.scotland/mb.ashx
- British Genealogy: Sub-Forums: Scotland
  www.british-genealogy.com/forums
  Scroll down and click on 'Scotland'
- The Scotland Genweb Project: Query Boards for all of Scotland
  www.scotlandgenweb.org/viewpage.php?page_id=3
- UK Genealogy: Mailing Lists
  www.ukgenealogy.co.uk/lists.htm
  List of those hosted by Rootsweb

6. County Pages

A great deal of information is to be found on genealogical county and local pages. A few individuals have created their own pages, but four organizations have provided pages for every Scottish county. Genuki provides some of the most useful pages, concentrating attention on primary historical information, rather than ongoing and completed research. It has many pages on particular parishes (which are not separately listed here). Authoritative parish pages are also provided by Family Search's Research Wiki. These include full details of microfilm available through the Latter-Day Saints Family History Centres, and of other parish records available elsewhere. Genweb offers more general information, including query boards for each county, and more information on current and completed family history research. UKGenealogy offers a range of information on general and commercial resources.

Aberdeenshire
- Aberdeenshire Genuki
  www.urie.demon.co.uk/genuki/ABD
- Aberdeenshire Genweb
  www.scotlandgenweb.org/viewpage.php?page_id=2
- Aberdeenshire-Scotland (ABD) UK Genealogy
  www.ukgenealogy.co.uk/abd.htm
- Family Search Research Wiki: Aberdeenshire, Scotland
  https://wiki.familysearch.org/en/Aberdeenshire,_Scotland_Parishes
- N.E. Scotland Genealogy
  http://myweb.tiscali.co.uk/nescotland
  Covering Aberdeenshire & Kincardineshire

Angus
- Angus Genuki
  www.genuki.org.uk/big/sct/ANS

- Angus Scotland Genweb
  www.scotlandgenweb.org/viewpage.php?page_id=7
- Angus-Scotland (ANS): UK Genealogy
  www.ukgenealogy.co.uk/ans.htm
- Family Search Research Wiki: Angus (or Forfarshire), Scotland
  https://wiki.familysearch.org/en/Angus_(or_Forfarshire),_Scotland
- Dundee Roots.com
  www.dundeeroots.com

Argyll
- Argyll Genuki
  www.genuki.org.uk/big/sct/ARL
- Argyllshire Genweb
  www.scotlandroyalty.org/argyll/argyllshire.html
- Argyll-Scotland (ARL) UK Genealogy
  www.ukgenealogy.co.uk/arl.htm
- Family Search Research Wiki: Argyllshire, Scotland
  https://wiki.familysearch.org/en/Argyllshire,_Scotland
- Family History Resources for Colonsay and Oransay
  www.colonsay.org.uk/Colonsay%20Records.html
  Click 'History' for further pages on Genealogy
- Hebridean Connections
  www.hebrideanconnections.com/home.aspx
  Database covering many sources from Argyll, Invernessshire, &
  Ross & Cromarty
- Knapdale People
  www.knapdalepeople.com
  Includes various databases
- Mull Genealogy
  www.mullgenealogy.co.uk
- Skipness Parish, Argyllshire, Scotland, Records
  www.rootsweb.com/~sctcskip/Skipness.htm
  Includes a variety of original sources, some of them listed elsewhere in
  this directory
- Western Isles Genweb
  www.scotlandgenweb.org/viewpage.php?page_id=25
  Covers parts of Argyll, Invernessshire, and Ross & Cromarty

Ayrshire
- Ayrshire Genuki
  www.genuki.org.uk/big/sct/AYR
- Ayrshire Scotland Genealogy: A Scotland Genweb Project Site
  www.rootsweb.com/~sctayr/index.html
- Ayrshire UK Genealogy
  www.ukgenealogy.co.uk/ayr.htm
- Ayrshire Roots
  www.ayrshire-roots.com
- Family Search Research Wiki: Ayrshire, Scotland
  https://wiki.familysearch.org/en/Ayrshire,_Scotland
- Ayrshire on the Net
  www.webring.com/hub?ring=clyde
  Webring
- Maybole Home Page
  www.maybole.org

Banffshire
- Banffshire Genuki
  www.abdnet.co.uk/genuki/BAN
  There are many pages listing kirk session records for particular
  parishes on this site, which are not listed separately here.
- Family Search Research Wiki: Banffshire, Scotland
  https://wiki.familysearch.org/en/Banffshire,_Scotland
- The Scotland Genweb Project: Banffshire
  www.scotlandgenweb.org/viewpage.php?page_id=10
- UK Genealogy: Banffshire, Scotland (BAN)
  www.ukgenealogy.co.uk/ban.htm

Berwickshire
- Berwickshire Genuki
  www.genuki.org.uk/big/sct/BEW
- Berwickshire, Scotland
  www.rootsweb.ancestry.com/~sctbew
  Genweb page
- Family Search Research Wiki: Berwickshire, Scotland
  https://wiki.familysearch.org/en/Berwickshire,_Scotland

- UK Genealogy: Berwickshire, Scotland (BEW):
  www.ukgenealogy.co.uk/bew.htm
- Heritage Hub Source List: Tracing Scottish Border Ancestors
  www.heartofhawick.co.uk/heritagehub/collections/sbancestors.pdf
  Covers Berwickshire, Peeblesshire, Roxburghshire, & Selkirkshire

Buteshire
- Buteshire Genuki
  www.genuki.org.uk/big/sct/BUT
- Buteshire Scotland Genealogy: a Scotland Genweb Project Site
  www.scotlandgenweb.org/buteshire
- Family Search Research Wiki: Buteshire, Scotland
  https://wiki.familysearch.org/en/Buteshire,_Scotland
- UK Genealogy: Buteshire - Scotland (BUT)
  www.ukgenealogy.co.uk/but.htm

Caithness
- Family Search Research Wiki: Caithness, Scotland
  https://wiki.familysearch.org/en/Caithness-shire,_Scotland
- Genuki: Caithness County
  www.frayston.demon.co.uk/genuki/cai
  www.genuki.org.uk/big/sct/CAI
- UK Genealogy: Caithness - Scotland (CAI)
  www.ukgenealogy.co.uk/cai.htm

Clackmannanshire
- Clackmannanshire Genuki
  www.dgnscrn.demon.co.uk/genuki/CLK/
- Family Search Research Wiki: Clackmannanshire, Scotland
  https://wiki.familysearch.org/en/Clackmannanshire,_Scotland
- The Scotland Genweb Project: Clackmannanshire
  www.scotlandgenweb.org/viewpage.php?page_id=11
- UK Genealogy: Clackmannanshire - Scotland (CLK)
  www.ukgenealogy.co.uk/clk.htm

Dumfriesshire
- Dumfriesshire Genuki
  www.genuki.org.uk/big/sct/DFS

- Dumfriesshire Scotland Genweb Project
  www.rootsweb.com/~sctdfs
- Family Search Research Wiki: Dumfries-shire, Scotland
  https://wiki.familysearch.org/en/Dumfries-shire,_Scotland
- UK Genealogy: Dumfries-shire - Scotland (DFS)
  www.ukgenealogy.co.uk/dfs.htm
- The Scottish Page, dedicated to the research of Scottish Ancestry, especially that of Dumfries-Galloway
  http://homepages.rootsweb.com/~scottish

Dunbartonshire
- Dunbartonshire Genuki
  www.genuki.org.uk/big/sct/DNB
- Dunbartonshire County, Scotland: a Scotland Genweb Project
  www.rootsweb.com/~sctdnb
- Family Search Research Wiki: Dunbartonshire, Scotland
  https://wiki.familysearch.org/en/Dunbartonshire,_Scotland
- UK Genealogy: Dunbartonshire - Scotland (DNB)
  www.ukgenealogy.co.uk/dnb.htm

East Lothian
- East Lothian Genuki
  www.clerkington.plus.com/GENUKI/ELN
- Family Search Research Wiki: East Lothian (or Haddington shire), Scotland
  https://wiki.familysearch.org/en/East_Lothian_(or_
  Haddingtonshire),_Scotland
- The Scotland Genweb Project: East Lothian
  www.scotlandgenweb.org/viewpage.php?page_id=14
- UK Genealogy: East Lothian - Scotland (ELN)
  www.ukgenealogy.co.uk/eln.htm

Fife
- Family Search Research Wiki: Fife, Scotland
  https://wiki.familysearch.org/en/Fife,_Scotland
- Fife Genuki
  www.genuki.org.uk/big/sct/FIF
- Fife Scotland Genweb
  www.rootsweb.com/~sctfif

- UK Genealogy: Fife - Scotland (FIF)
  www.ukgenealogy.co.uk/fif.htm
- The Fife Post: Genealogy in Fife
  www.thefifepost.com/genealogy.htm

Forfarshire
See Angus

Invernessshire
See also Argyll
- Family Search Research Wiki: Inverness-shire, Scotland
  https://wiki.familysearch.org/en/Inverness-shire,_Scotland
- Inverness-shire Genuki
  www.genuki.org.uk/big/sct/INV
- Inverness, Scotland [Genweb]
  www.jansdigs.com/Inverness
- UK Genealogy: Inverness-shire - Scotland (INV)
  www.ukgenealogy.co.uk/inv.htm
- Isle of Muck History: Genealogy Information
  www.islemuck.com/geneal.htm

Kincardineshire
See also Aberdeenshire
- Family Search Research Wiki: Kincardineshire, Scotland
  https://wiki.familysearch.org/en/Kincardineshire,_Scotland
- Kincardineshire Genuki
  www.genuki.org.uk/big/sct/KCD
- The Scotland Genweb Project: Kincardineshire
  www.scotlandgenweb.org/viewpage.php?page_id=12
- UK Genealogy: Kincardineshire - Scotland (KCD)
  www.ukgenealogy.co.uk/kcd.htm

Kinrossshire
- Family Search Research Wiki: Kinross-shire, Scotland
  https://wiki.familysearch.org/en/Kinross-shire,_Scotland
- Kinross-shire Genuki
  www.dgnscrn.demon.co.uk/genuki/KRS

- Kinross-Shire [Genweb]
  www.rootsweb.ancestry.com/~sctkrs
- UK Genealogy: Kinross-shire - Scotland (KRS)
  www.ukgenealogy.co.uk/krs.htm
- Exploring Kinross's history
  www.kinrossmuseum.co.uk/history.html

Kirkcudbrightshire
- Family Search Research Wiki: Kirkcudbrightshire, Scotland
  https://wiki.familysearch.org/en/Kirkcudbrightshire,_Scotland
- Kirkcudbrightshire Genuki
  www.genuki.org.uk/big/sct/KKD
- Kirkcudbrightshire [Genweb]
  www.scotlandgenweb.org/viewpage.php?page_id=13
- UK Genealogy: Kirkcudbrightshire - Scotland (KKD)
  www.ukgenealogy.co.uk/kkd.htm
- Old Kirkcudbright
  www.old-kirkcudbright.net
  Includes page on genealogy

Lanarkshire
- Family Search Research Wiki: Lanarkshire, Scotland
  https://wiki.familysearch.org/en/Lanarkshire,_Scotland
- Lanarkshire Genuki
  www.genuki.org.uk/big/sct/LKS
- UK Genealogy: Lanarkshire - Scotland (LKS)
  www.ukgenealogy.co.uk/lks.htm
- Lanark(shire) Miscellany
  www.scottap.com/family/Lanark
  Includes miscellaneous transcripts, *etc.*

Midlothian
- Family Search Research Wiki: Midlothian (Edinburghshire), Scotland
  https://wiki.familysearch.org/en/Midlothian_
  (Edinburghshire),_Scotland
- Midlothian Genuki
  www.genuki.org.uk/big/sct/MLN

- The Midlothianshire Scotland Genweb Project
  www.rootsweb.com/~sctmln
- UK Genealogy: Midlothian - Scotland (MLN)
  www.ukgenealogy.co.uk/mln.htm
- Duddingston
  www.ancestor.abel.co.uk/Duddingston.html
- Inveresk (Midlothian)
  www.ancestor.abel.co.uk/Inveresk.html
- Liberton (Midlothian)
  www.ancestor.abel.co.uk/Liberton.html
- Newton (Midlothian)
  www.ancestor.abel.co.uk/Newton.html

Moray
- Family Search Research Wiki: Moray or Elginshire
  https://wiki.familysearch.org/en/Moray_or_Elginshire,_Scotland
- Moray Genuki
  www.genuki.org.uk/big/sct/MOR/index.html
- The Scotland Genweb Project: Moray
  www.scotlandgenweb.org/viewpage.php?page_id=18
- UK Genealogy: Morayshire - Scotland (MOR)
  www.ukgenealogy.co.uk/mor.htm

Nairnshire
- Family Search Research Wiki: Nairnshire, Scotland
  https://wiki.familysearch.org/en/Nairnshire,_Scotland
- Nairnshire Genuki
  www.genuki.org.uk/big/sct/NAI
- The Scotland GenWeb Project: Nairnshire
  www.scotlandgenweb.org/viewpage.php?page_id=19
- UK Genealogy: Nairnshire - Scotland (NAI)
  www.ukgenealogy.co.uk/nai.htm

Orkney
- Family Search Research Wiki: Orkney, Scotland
  https://wiki.familysearch.org/en/Orkney,_Scotland
- Orkney Genuki
  www.genuki.org.uk/big/sct/OKI

- The Scotland GenWeb Project: Orkney
  www.scotlandgenweb.org/viewpage.php?page_id=20
- UK Genealogy: Orkney - Scotland (OKI)
  www.ukgenealogy.co.uk/oki.htm
- Orkney Genealogy: Family Heritage of the Orkney Islands of Scotland
  www.cursiter.com
- Rousay Roots
  www.rousayroots.com

Peeblesshire
- Family Search Research Wiki: Peebles-shire, Scotland
  https://wiki.familysearch.org/en/Peebles-shire,_Scotland
- Peeblesshire Genuki
  www.genuki.org.uk:8080/big/sct/PEE
- The Scotland Genweb Project: Peeblesshire
  www.scotlandgenweb.org/viewpage.php?page_id=21
- UK Genealogy: Peebles-shire - Scotland (PEE)
  www.ukgenealogy.co.uk/pee.htm

Perthshire
- Family Search Research Wiki: Perthshire, Scotland
  https://wiki.familysearch.org/en/Perthshire,_Scotland
- Perthshire Genuki
  www.genuki.org.uk/big/sct/PER
- Perthshire: Scotland GenWeb Project
  www.rootsweb.com/~sctper
- UK Genealogy: Perthshire - Scotland (PER)
  www.ukgenealogy.co.uk/per.htm
- Genealogy: Rannoch Net
  www.rannoch.net/Genealogy.htm

Renfrewshire
- Family Search Research Wiki: Renfrewshire, Scotland
  https://wiki.familysearch.org/en/Renfrewshire,_Scotland
- Renfrewshire Genuki
  www.genuki.org.uk/big/sct/RFW

- Renfrewshire Scotland GenWeb Project
  www.scotlandgenweb.org/viewpage.php?page_id=22
- UK Genealogy Renfrewshire - Scotland (RFW)
  www.ukgenealogy.co.uk/rfw.htm

Ross & Cromarty
See also Argyll
- Family Search Research Wiki: Ross & Cromarty, Scotland
  https://wiki.familysearch.org/en/Ross_%26_Cromarty,_Scotland
- Ross & Cromarty (includes parts of Lewis)
  www.genuki.org.uk/big/sct/ROC
- Ross and Cromarty: Scotland GenWeb Project
  www.rootsweb.ancestry.com/~sctroc
- UK Genealogy: Ross & Cromarty - Scotland (ROC)
  www.ukgenealogy.co.uk/roc.htm
- Some Coigach Genealogy
  http://freepages.genealogy.rootsweb.ancestry.com/~coigach/
  Includes census extracts, militia lists, *etc.*

Roxburghshire
- Family Search Research Wiki: Roxburghshire, Scotland
  https://wiki.familysearch.org/en/Roxburghshire,_Scotland
- Roxburghshire Genuki
  www.genuki.org.uk/big/sct/ROX
- UK Genealogy: Roxburghshire - Scotland (ROX)
  www.ukgenealogy.co.uk/rox.htm

Selkirkshire
- Family Search Research Wiki: Selkirkshire, Scotland
  https://wiki.familysearch.org/en/Selkirkshire,_Scotland
- Selkirkshire Genuki
  www.genuki.org.uk/big/sct/SEL
- Scotland GenWeb: Selkirkshire Genealogy Project
  www.scotlandgenweb.org/~selkirkshire
- UK Genealogy: Selkirkshire - Scotland (SEL)
  www.ukgenealogy.co.uk/sel.htm

Shetland
- Family Search Research Wiki: Shetland (or Zetland), Scotland
  https://wiki.familysearch.org/en/Shetland_(or_Zetland),_
  Scotland_Parishes

- Shetland Genuki
  www.genuki.org.uk/big/sct/SHI
- Shetland Islands Genweb Project
  www.scotlandgenweb.org/shetland
- UK Genealogy: Shetland - Scotland (SHI)
  www.ukgenealogy.co.uk/shi.htm
- Shetland Family History Homepage
  http://bayanne.info/Shetland

Stirlingshire
- Family Search Research Wiki: Stirlingshire, Scotland
  https://wiki.familysearch.org/en/Stirlingshire_Parishes
- Stirlingshire Genuki
  www.dgnscrn.demon.co.uk/genuki/STI
- UK Genealogy: Stirlingshire - Scotland (STI)
  www.ukgenealogy.co.uk/sti.htm

Sutherland
See also Invernessshire
- Family Search Research Wiki: Sutherland, Scotland
  https://wiki.familysearch.org/en/Sutherland,_Scotland_Parishes
- Sutherland Genuki
  www.genuki.org.uk/big/sct/SUT
- County Sutherland
  www.countysutherland.co.uk/index.html
- Sutherland Scotland Genweb
  www.scotlandgenweb.org/sutherland
- UK Genealogy: Sutherland - Scotland (SUT)
  www.ukgenealogy.co.uk/sut.htm

West Lothian
- Family Search Research Wiki: West Lothian (Linlithgowshire),
  Scotland
  https://wiki.familysearch.org/en/West_Lothian_(Linlithgow
  shire),_Scotland_Parishes
- West Lothian (Linlithgowshire) Genuki
  www.genuki.org.uk/big/sct/WLN

- The West Lothian Scotland GenWeb Project
  www.scotlandgenweb.org/~westlothian
- UK Genealogy: West Lothian, Scotland (WLN)
  www.ukgenealogy.co.uk/wln.htm

Wigtownshire
- Family Search Research Wiki: Wigtonshire, Scotland
  https://wiki.familysearch.org/en/Wigtonshire,_Scotland_Parishes
- Wigtownshire Genuki
  www.genuki.org.uk/big/sct/WIG
- Wigtownshire Scotland [GenWeb]
  www.rootsweb.ancestry.com/~sctwig/wigtown.html
- UK Genealogy: Wigtownshire - Scotland (WIG)
  www.ukgenealogy.co.uk/wig.htm
- The Wigtownshire Pages
  http://freepages.history.rootsweb.ancestry.com/~leighann

7. Surnames

The Internet is an invaluable aid for those who want to make contact with others researching the same surname. There are innumerable personal and family web-pages, surname mailing lists, and lists of surname interests. Gateways for family web-sites and surname mailing lists are listed here, as are surname interest lists.

Family Web Pages
A number of international sites offer gateways to websites for specific surnames - although they all have an American bias:
- Cyndis List: Personal Home Pages Index
  www.cyndislist.com/personal.htm
  Good starting point
- Cyndis List: Surnames, Family Association, & Family News-letters Index
  www.cyndislist.com/surnames.htm
- Registry of Web Sites at Rootsweb
  www.rootsweb.ancestry.com/~websites/
  Scroll down to 'Surname Websites". Probably the most extensive listing of surname sites

For a directory of Scottish clans and families, visit:
- Scottish Clans and Families
  www.usscots.com/clan/

A number of surname specific databases are hosted at:
- Scotsfind: Scottish Genealogy Databases
  www.scotsfind.org/surnamedatabases_free/freesurnameindex.htm

Buteshire
- List of Bute Researchers Home Pages
  www.scotlandgenweb.org/buteshire/homepage.htm

Orkney
- Orkney Genealogies on the Web
  www.genuki.org.uk/big/sct/OKI/Families.html
  List of family homepages

Surname Mailing Lists
Chapter 5 should be consulted for general advice on identifying mailing lists. A wide variety of websites, and all Rootsweb message boards, can be searched at:
- Surname Helper Home Page
  http://surhelp.rootsweb.ancestry.com

See also:
- Surname Resources at Rootsweb
  http://resources.rootsweb.ancestry.com/surnames

Surname Interests
Many sites provide names and addresses of researchers seeking information on particular surnames. The most substantial of these sites (international in scope) is:
- Rootsweb Surname List
  http://rsl.rootsweb.ancestry.com

Other major sites include:
- Surname Lists
  www.genuki.org.uk/indexes/SurnamesLists.html
- Family History UK: Wanted Names Adverts
  www.familyhistory.uk.com
  Interests list. Click on `Wanted Names' and `Scotland'
- Online Scottish Names Directory
  www.list.jaunay.com/sctnames
  Interest lists for Aberdeenshire, Ayrshire, Berwickshire, Buteshire, inc Arran, Caithness, Dumfriesshire, Dunbartonshire, East Lothian, Invernessshire, Kincardineshire, Kirkcudbrightshire, Lanarkshire, Midlothian, Moray, Nairnshire, Orkney, Peeblesshire, Perthshire, Ross & Cromarty, Roxburghshire, Selkirkshire, Shetland, Stirlingshire, & Wigtownshire

- Genealogical Research Directory
  www.lareau.org/grd.html
  Webpage for ordering the major published directory, as a book or CD

Many Scottish interests are posted on:
- Curious Fox
  www.curiousfox.com

A surname index to 10 different databases is provided at:
- Surname Navigator: Scotland
  www.geneaservice.nl/navigator/scotland

Angus
- Angus Surnames List
  www.jimjar.net/Angus

Argyll
- Argyllshire, Scotland Surnames & Queries
  http://genealogy.about.com/cs/argyllsurnames
- People who are researching specific surnames in regards to the Isle of Islay
  http://homepages.rootsweb.com/~steve/islay/surnames.htm

Ayrshire
- Ayrshire Surnames Database
  www.ayrshire-roots.co.uk/surnames.php
- Maybole Surname Interests
  www.maybole.org/history/Surnames/surnamesac.htm

Banffshire
- Banffshire Surname List
  www.rootsweb.com/~sctban

Berwickshire
- Borders Family History Society: Interests Search
  www.bordersfhs.org.uk/BFHSInterestsIndexSearch.asp
  Covers Berwickshire, Roxburghshire, Peeblesshire, & Selkirkshire

Caithness
- Highlands Family History Society Interests Surname Search
www.highlandfhs.org.uk/HFHSInterestsIndexSearch.asp
Covers Caithness, Sutherland, Ross & Cromarty, Invernessshire, and Nairnshire

Clackmannanshire
- Genuki Clackmannanshire Surname List
www.dgnscrn.demon.co.uk/genuki/CLK/misc/surnames
- Central Scotland Family History Society: Members Interests
www.csfhs.org.uk/members_interest.htm
Covers Clackmannanshire, West Perthshire, Stirlingshire, & parts of West Lothian

Dunbartonshire
- Dunbartonshire Surnames List
www.rootsweb.ancestry.com/~sctdnb/surnames.html

East Lothian
- The Lothians Family History Society: Members Interests
www.lothiansfhs.org/?q=node/20
Covers East Lothian, Midlothian, and West Lothian

Fife
- Kingdom of Fife Surnames List
www.genuki.org.uk/big/scot/Fife/fife.surnames.html

Invernessshire
See also Caithness
- Inverness-shire, Scotland, Surname Registry
freepages.genealogy.rootsweb.com/~ked1/Invreg1.html

Kinrossshire
- Genuki Kinross-shire Surname List
www.dgnscrn.demon.co.uk/genuki/KRS/misc/surnames

Lanarkshire
- The Lanarkshire Surname List
www.rootsweb.com/~sctlks

- Glasgow & West of Scotland Family History Society: Online Members' Interests Directory
www.gwsfhs.org.uk/omid/default.aspx

Midlothian
See East Lothian

Nairnshire
See Caithness

Orkney
- Orkney Family History Researchers
www.genuki.org.uk/big/sct/OKI/famhist.html
Interests list

Peeblesshire
See Berwickshire

Perthshire
See Clackmannanshire

Renfrewshire
- Renfrewshire Surnames List
http://freepages.genealogy.rootsweb.ancestry.com/
~renfrewshire/index.htm

Ross & Cromarty
See Caithness

Roxburghshire
See Berwickshire

Selkirkshire
See Berwickshire

Stirlingshire
See Clackmannanshire

Sutherland
See Caithness

West Lothian
See also Clackmannanshire and East Lothian
* West Lothian Family History Society: Members Interests
  www.wlfhs.org.uk
  Click on side-bar

8. Births, Marriages and Deaths

One of the most important sites for Scottish family historians is `Scotlands People'. It provides full coverage of the old parish registers, and of the statutory registers as far as the demands of privacy allow. Begin by reading these two pages:

* Scotlands People: Old Parish Registers
  www.scotlandspeople.gov.uk/content/help/index.aspx?r=554&613
  Pay per view site. Indexes and digitised images of births/baptisms, banns/marriages, and (a very few) deaths/burials from the old parish registers.
* Scotlands People: Statutory Registers
  www.scotlandspeople.gov.uk/content/help/index.aspx?r=554&612
  Pay per view site. Includes indexes of births marriages and deaths, 1855-2006, with images of births (1855-1908), marriages (1855-1933) and deaths (1855-1958)

See also:
* General Register Office for Scotland
  www.gro-scotland.gov.uk/famrec
  Details of Old Parish Registers and Civil Registers, *etc.*
* Family Search Research Wiki: Scotland: Research Strategies for Locating Births Marriages and Deaths
  https://wiki.familysearch.org/en/Scotland:_Research_Strategies_for_Locating_Births_Marriages_and_Deaths•
* National Library of Scotland: Family History: Births Deaths and Marriages
  www.nls.uk/family-history/births-deaths-marriages/
                                    index.html#mckirdy
  Lists useful resources held by the library

* Death and Burial
  www.scan.org.uk/knowledgebase/topics/ deathandburial_topic.htm
* Records of Death and Burial
  www.scan.org.uk/knowledgebase/topics/deathandburial_
                                    records.htm

- Pre-1855 baptism record transcripts and indexes
  www.scotlandspeoplehub.gov.uk/pdf/Pre-1855%20baptisms.pdf
  Held by Scotlands People Hub

For an important international index to baptisms and marriages, which includes many Scottish entries, visit:
- International Genealogical Index
  www.familysearch.org
  Click 'search' and title. Make sure you read the 'tips' page before searching. For a general discussion of this important index, see:
- International Genealogical Index
  www.genuki.org.uk/big/eng/LIN/igi.html

For cemetery registers, try:
- Deceased Online
  www.deceasedonline.com
  Database of cemetery registers, mostly English, but including 190,000 records from Angus. More are likely to be added

Civil Registration
- Family Search Research Wiki: Scotland Civil Registration: Vital Records
  **https://wiki.familysearch.org/en/Scotland_Civil_
  Registration-_Vital_Records**
- 1855 Civil Registration Records: A Virtual Treasure Trove of Information
  **http://freepages.history.rootsweb.ancestry.com/~leighann/
  1855s/all_1855s.html**
- The Scottish Way of Birth and Death: from the Records of the Registrar General for Scotland, 1855-1939
  www.gla.ac.uk/departments/scottishwayofbirthanddeath
  History of registratrion

Old Parish Registers
- FreeReg
  www.freereg.org.uk
  Project to provide free indexes to the old parish registers *etc.* Click 'Counties and Parishes' and scroll down to see county pages, which give details of Scottish registers indexed. These pages are not separately listed below

- Birth, Marriage and Death Records in Scotland
  www.ktb.net/~dwills/scotref/13302-bmdtables.htm
  List of LDS films
- Scotland BDM Exchange
  www.sctbdm.com
- Scottish Marriage Index
  www.mlfhs.org.uk
  Click 'Anglo-Scottish' and scroll down
- SCT Scottish Deaths 1747-1868
  **www.worldvitalrecords.com/indexinfo.aspx?ix=scotland_
  death_records_1747-1868**
  Index to registers from Midlothian, East Lothian, Fife, *etc.* Pay per view
- Irregular Border and Scottish Runaway Marriages
  www.gro-scotland.gov.uk/famrec/sumrmar.html
  List of registers
- Illegitimacy: recording of illegitimate births and baptisms
  www.scotlandspeople.gov.uk/content/help/index.aspx?r=551&578
- UK Parish Baptism Marriage and Burial Records
  http://www.ancestry.co.uk/search/rectype/vital/epr/main.aspx
  Index to various published registers for many counties

Roman Catholic Registers
- CPR Births and Baptisms
  www.scotlandspeople.gov.uk/content/help/index.aspx?r=554&1374
  Pay per view site

Nonconformist Registers
- Miscellaneous Records (MR) containing entries from Non-Conformist churches relevant to the Old Parish Registers
  www.scotlandspeoplehub.gov.uk/pdf/list-of-oprs-appendix3.pdf

Aberdeenshire

Strathdon
- Strathdon Vital Records: OPR Parochial Registers
  http://sites.google.com/site/strathdonvitals
  Transcripts of old parish registers and of civil registers

Angus

- Non-conformist Church Records in Angus and Dundee
  www.dundeeroots.com/nonconformist.htm
- List of Statutorily Registered Deaths in 1855, for Districts in Angus,
  Scotland (Years 1855 to 1875, 1881 and 1891 for Monikie, Angus and
  Errol, Perthshire)
  www.monikie.org.uk/1855deaths-in-angus.htm

Barry

- Burial Records from the Barry, Angus, Scotland Parish Register,
  1746-1812
  **http://freepages.genealogy.rootsweb.com/~pinks/scotland/
  angus/barry.htm**
  In progress
- Parish of Barry, Angus, Scotland OPR: Burials 1746 to 1812
  http://freepages.genealogy.rootsweb.com/~shellypages/BurIdx.htm
- Extract from the Old Parish Register for the Parish of Barry, Angus,
  Scotland: Burials 1757-1812
  www.monikie.org.uk/ah-barryopr.htm

Benvie
See Liff

Dundee

- Cemeteries & Graveyards: Dundee City Archives: Guide to
  death/burial records: Dundee & its Environs
  www.dundeeroots.com/burials.htm
- Dundee Genealogy Unit
  www.dundeecity.gov.uk/archive/genealogyunit
- Friends of Dundee City Archives: Databases
  www.fdca.org.uk/FDCADatabases.html
  Includes Wesleyan register of baptisms, Dundee 1785-1898, and
  burial records for the Howff, Dundee City's cemetery
- Extract from the old parish register for the Dundee (St. Peter
  parish), Scotland burials 1837-1856
  www.monikie.org.uk/ah-saintpeter.htm
- Deaths Registered at Dundee, Scotland, 1990 to 1993
  www.monikie.org.uk/ah-dundeedeaths.htm
  Over 6,500 names

- Deaths recorded in Dundee, Scotland from 01-04-1990 - 19-03-1993.
  www.monikie.org.uk/dundee-deaths-010490-190393.txt

Dunnichen

- Dunnichen Parish, Angus, Scotland: Interments 1856-76
  www.monikie.org.uk/ah-dunnichen1856-76.htm

Monikie

- Monikie Kirkyard Burial Records extracted from the Old Parish
  Records
  www.monikie.org.uk/ah-monburtext.htm
- Death Records extracted from the Statutory Registration Records
  for the years 1855 to 1875, 1881 & 1891.
  www.monikie.org.uk/monikiestatdeaths.htm
  For Monikie
- Monikie Parish (Kirk). Various Lists for Death, *etc.,* Records and Burials
  www.monikie.org.uk/ah-monikieburialslist.htm

Argyll

Bowmore

- `OPR`: Old Parish Records
  http://homepages.rootsweb.ancestry.com/~steve/islay/opr/
  Bowmore & Killarow baptisms 1763-1854, & marriages 1771-1854;
  Kildalton baptisms 1723-1856, & marriages 1722-66 & 1789-1856

Colonsay

- Family History Resources for Colonsay and Oransay
  www.colonsay.org.uk/Colonsay%20Records.html
  Includes pages for baptisms, marriages, & deaths, 1796-1854

Islay

- Index to Islay Civil Registration for Marriages 1855 - 1875, 188 and
  1891 / Monta Salmon
  **http://homepages.rootsweb.ancestry.com/~steve/islay/civil/
  islay_ma.htm**
- Islay Birth/Baptism Records
  http://freepages.family.rootsweb.ancestry.com/~tlarson/bdm/births/
  For Kilarrow 1763-1854, Kildalton, 1723-1856, Kilchoman,1820-54,
  Kilmeny 1802-55, Oa, 1833-55, and Portnahaven 1832-55

- Islay Marriage Records
  http://freepages.family.rootsweb.ancestry.com/~tlarson/bdm/marriages/
  For Kilarrow 1771-1854, Kildalton 1722-66 & 1789-1854,Kilchoman 1820-54, Oa 1833-54, and Portnahaven 1833-54; civil registers 1855-75.
- Islay Death Records
  http://freepages.family.rootsweb.ancestry.com/~tlarson/bdm/deaths
  Covers 1855-75
- LDS / Mormon Church Records
  http://homepages.rootsweb.ancestry.com/~steve/islay/lds_fiche.htm
  For the Isle of Islay

Kilarow
See Bowmore and Islay

Kilchoman
See Islay

Kildalton
See Bowmore and Islay

Kilmeny
See Islay

Mull
- Mull Genealogy: Burial Place Index
  www.mullgenealogy.co.uk
  Click title. Index to burials on Mull, and to Mull burials overseas

Oa
See Islay

Portnahaven
See Islay

Skipness
- Skipness Parish Marriages, Argyllshire, Scotland
  www.rootsweb.com/~sctcship/skipness_marr.txt
  1800-21

Ayrshire
- *Ayrshire Herald* BDM Database: *Ardrossan and Saltcoats Herald* BDM Intimation Database
  www.ayrshire-roots.co.uk/ash.php
  Index, 1856-1929
- Ayrshire Roots: Burials
  www.ayrshireroots.com/Genealogy/Records/Burial/Burial.htm
  Lists of cemeteries & registers
- Ayrshire Roots: Civil Registration
  www.ayrshireroots.com/Genealogy/Records/Post%201855/Post%201855.htm
  Includes transcripts of some post-1855 records
- Ayrshire Roots: Old Parish Registers
  www.ayrshireroots.com/Genealogy/Records/OPR/OPR.htm
  Includes list
- [Ayrshire BMD Database]
  www.ayrshireroots.com/Genealogy/Reference/Ayr%20Births_files/Ayr%20Births_files.htm

Dalrymple
- Dalrymple Old Parish Registers
  www.geographyhigh.connectfree.co.uk/famhist/dalrympleoprmenu.html
  Covers 1699-1854

Kilwinning
- Registers of Burials in Kilwinning Parochial Cemetery 1870-1897
  www.ayrshireroots.com/Towns/Kilwinning/Kilwinning%20Burials%201870.htm

Stair
- Stair Parish Church Baptismal Register 1862-1917
  http://stairchurch.homestead.com/Baptismal.html

Banffshire
- Civil Register of Births, Deaths and Marriages: LDS Film Numbers
  www.abdnet.co.uk/genuki/BAN/LDSfilmsBDM.html
  For Banffshire

Berwickshire

Berwick upon Tweed
- Marriages in Berwick 1865
  http://freepages.genealogy.rootsweb.ancestry.com/
  ~connochie/bdm/bewmarr1865.html

- Deaths in Berwick 1855
  http://freepages.genealogy.rootsweb.ancestry.com/
  ~connochie/bdm/bewdeaths1855.html
  Continued as follows:
  1868 **/bewdeaths1868.html**
  1872 **/bewdeaths1872.htm**
  1881 **/bewdeaths1881.htm**

Bunkle
- The Session Book of Bunkle and Preston, 1665-1690 / James Hardy (ed)
  www.archive.org/stream/sessionbookbunk00clubgoog
  /sessionbookbunk00clubgoog_djvu.txt
  Originally published Berwickshire Naturalist Club, 1900. Includes
  register of baptisms and marriages, tombstone inscriptions, etc.

Coldingham
- Viv Dunstan's indexes: Coldingham mortcloth index, 1694-1759
  www.vivdunstan.co.uk/indexes/coldmort.html
  An off-line index to c.4,000 burials; the mortcloth was hired out
  to cover coffins.

Preston
See Bunkle

Buteshire
- Buteshire Genealogy Research
  www.members.shaw.ca/Buteshire
  Index of births, marriages and deaths submitted by users
- Buteshire Research Database
  www.members.shaw.ca/Buteshire
  Birth, death & marriage exchange

Clackmannanshire
- LDS Film Records for the Clackmannanshire Parishes
  www.dgnscrn.demon.co.uk/genuki/CLK/misc/LDSfilms.html
  List of old parish register extracts, census returns, and birth, marriage
  and death records in Latter Day Saints Family History Centres

Dumfriesshire
- Irregular Border and Scottish Runaway Marriages
  www.gro-scotland.gov.uk/famrec/hlpsrch/summar/runmar.html

East Lothian

Bolton
- Parish Register
  www.ndhm.org.uk/page_6.htm
  For Bolton and Saltoun, 1998-2008

Prestonpans
- Prestonpans Marriages
  www.ancestor.abel.co.uk/Prestonpans.html
  Prestonpans marriages from the registers of Edinburgh, 1595-1800, &
  Inveresk,1719-50.

Saltoun
See also Bolton
- Proclamations of Banns in Saltoun, 1929 - 1977
  www.ndhm.org.uk/page_11.htm

Fife
- The Old Parish Registers of Fife
  www.fifefhs.org
  Click 'Records'
- Fife OPRs and Census Returns
  www.thefifepost.com/ocfife.htm
  List of records held in Kirkcaldy Central Library
- Detailed List of the Old Parochial Registers of Scotland: Fife
  www.genuki.org.uk/big/sct/FIF/DetailedListofOPRsAC.htm

- Births in Fife
  www.rootsweb.ancestry.com/~sctfif/ffbrths1.html
  Contributors entries, with their email addresses
- Brides in Fife
  www.rootsweb.ancestry.com/~sctfif/ffmrsb1.html
  Contributors entries, with their email addresses
- Grooms in Fife
  www.rootsweb.ancestry.com/~sctfif/ffmrsg1.html
- Deaths & Burials in Fife
  www.rootsweb.ancestry.com/~sctfif/ffdths1.html
  Contributors entries, with their email addresses
- Grooms in Fife
  www.rootsweb.ancestry.com/~sctfif/ffmrsg1.html

Anstruther
- Anstruther Free Church Births and Baptisms 1843-47
  www.fifefhs.org
  Click 'Records'

Anstruther Easter
- Anstruther-Easter Burials (1836-1854) from the Lair Register
  www.fifefhs.org/Records
  Click 'Records'

Auchtermuchty
- Auchtermuchty Free Church, later U.F.Martyrs Births Baptisms & Marriages 1843-1854
  www.fifefhs.org
  Click 'Records'

Balmerino
- Balmerino Deaths 1823-1854
  www.fifefhs.org
  Click 'Records'

Cairneyhill
- Cairneyhill Associate Baptisms 1746-1768
  www.fifefhs.org
  Click 'Records'

Cameron
- Cameron Burials 1842-1854
  www.fifefhs.org
  Click 'Records'

Ceres
- Ceres Associate Congregation: baptisms 1738-1806, 1808, 1836-37
  www.fifefhs.org
  Click 'Records'

Crail
- Associate Congregation, Crail: Baptisms 1821-1852 (with gaps)
  www.fifefhs.org
  Click 'Records'

Creich
- Creich and Flisk Free Church Baptisms and Marriages 1843-1854
  www.fifefhs.org
  Click 'Records'

Dunfermline
- Baptisms: North-Parish-Church, Dunfermline, 1851-1854
  www.fifefhs.org
  Click 'Records'
- St. Margaret's UP Church, Dunfermline: Baptisms 1851-1854
  www.fifefhs.org
  Click 'Records'

Dysart
- Dysart St. Serf's Interments (1795-1899)
  www.fifefhs.org
  Click 'Records'
- Dysart Relief Church: Baptisms 1828-1831
  www.fifefhs.org
  Click 'Records'

- Dysart St. Denis Interments, 1795-1861
  www.fifefhs.org
  Click 'Records'

Flisk
See Creich

Forgan
- Forgan Baptisms, 1695-1854 - listed by mother's maiden name
  www.twentytwoflassroad.co.uk/Newport/index.html
  Click on title

Invertiel
- Invertiel Baptisms 1844-1854
  www.fifefhs.org
  Click 'Records'

Kennoway
- Kennoway Baptisms 1848-1854: United Presbyterian Church
  www.fifefhs.org
  Click 'Records'

Kilconquhar
- Kilconquhar Burials 1847-1854
  www.fifefhs.org
  Click 'Records'

Kirkcaldy
- Bethelfield UP Church, Kirkcaldy: baptisms 1854-1854
  www.fifefhs.org
  Click 'Records'
- Kirkcaldy Burials 1767-1854
  www.fifefhs.org
  Click 'Records'

Leslie
- West United Presbyterian Church, Leslie: Baptisms 1849-1854
  www.fifefhs.org.uk
  Click 'Records'

Leven
- Leven Relief Church: Baptisms 1834-1854
  www.fifefhs.org
  Click 'Records'

Logie
- Logie Burials 1816-1854
  www.fifefhs.org
  Click 'Records'

Markinch
- Markinch Burials 1799-1854
  www.fifefhs.org
  Click 'Records'

Monimail
- Monimail Deaths 1848-1854 (from the communion roll, 1848-1862)
  www.fifefhs.org
  Click 'Records'

Newburgh
- Newburgh Associate Congregation: Marriages & Baptisms 1785-1812 & 1821-1849
  www.fifefhs.org
  Click 'Records'

Pathhead
- Pathhead Baptisms 1760-1854: Pathhead Associate Congregation
  www.fifefhs.org
  Click 'Records'

Pittenweem
- Pittenweem (St. Johns) Episcopal: Baptisms, Marriages & Deaths 1799-1854
  www.fifefhs.org
  Click 'Records'

Rathillet

- Rathillet Associate Congregation Baptisms & Marriages 1762-1840 (with gaps) from book 4 of Kirk Session records
  www.fifefhs.org
  Click 'Records'

Invernessshire

Glen

- Glen Baptisms 1866-1892
  http://freepages.genealogy.rootsweb.ancestry.com/~ked1/baptisms.html

Glen Urquhart

- Glen Urquhart Marriage Register
  http://freepages.genealogy.rootsweb.ancestry.com/~ked1/
  marriages.html

  1866-91

Kinrossshire

See also Perthshire
- LDS Film Records for the Kinross Parishes
  www.dgnscrn.demon.co.uk/genuki/KRS/misc/LDSfilms.html
  Parish registers, civil registration records, and census returns.

Kirkcudbrightshire

Buittle

- Buittle Old Parish Records
  http://buittle.org.uk/opr_s.htm
  Baptisms 1736-1856; marriages 1736-1854; burials 1761-1852; also Roman Catholic records 1764-1811

Kirkcudbright

- Deaths Recorded in Kirkcudbright OPRs
  www.old-kirkcudbright.net/genealogy/oprDeaths/index.asp
  For 1826-53

Munches

- Record of Marriages, Roman Catholic Church, Munches, Post 1747
  www.buittle.org.uk/neworder/munches/marriages.htm
  For births (not complete) see **/baptisms.htm**; for deaths, see **//deaths.htm**

Lanarkshire

- Civil Records for Lanark County 1855-1867
  www.ktb.net/~dwills/scotref/c-621-660a.htm
  Continued for 1868-1891 at **/c-621-660b.htm**. L.D.S. film numbers
- OPR Films for Lanark County
  www.ktb.net/~dwills/scotref/f-621-660.htm
  LDS film numbers

Midlothian

Canongate

See Holyrood & Liberton

Duddingston

- References to parish of Duddingston in the marriage register of the parish of Canongate, 1564-1800
  www.ancestor.abel.co.uk/dud/canm.html
- References to par. of Duddingston in the marriage register of the par. of Edinburgh, 1595-1700
  www.ancestor.abel.co.uk/dud/marra.html
  There are further pages covering 1701-1750 & 1751-1800

Edinburgh

See also Duddingston, Inveresk, Liberton and Prestonpans
- The Register of Marriages for the Parish of Edinburgh
  www.scotsfind.org/marriages_access/marriages.pdf
  Covers 1595-1800. Originally published by the Scottish Record Society.

Greyfriars

- Register of Interments in the Greyfriars Burying Ground, Edinburgh, 1658-1700
  www.scotsfind.org/greyfriars_access/greyfriars.pdf
  Originally published by the Scottish Record Society, 1902

Holyrood / Canongate

- Parish of Holyroodhouse or Canongate: Register of Marriages 1564-1800 / Francis J. Grant (ed.)
  www.scotsfind.org/canongate_access/canongate.pdf?
  Originally published by the Scottish Record Society

- Canongate Parish Burials: Edinburgh, Midlothian, Scotland 1820-1851
  www.scotsfind.org/databases_free/edinburgh.pdf

Inveresk
See also Prestonpans
- References to parish of Inveresk in the marriage register of the parish of Canongate, 1564-1800
  www.ancestor.abel.co.uk/inv/canm.html
- References to parish of Inveresk in the marriage register of the parish of Edinburgh, 1595-1700
  www.ancestor.abel.co.uk/inv/marra.html
  There are further pages covering 1701-1750 & 1751-1800

Liberton
- References to parish of Liberton in the marriage register of the parish of Canongate, 1564-1800
  www.ancestor.abel.co.uk/lib/canm.html
- References to par. of Liberton in the marriage register of the par. of Edinburgh, 1595-1700
  www.ancestor.abel.co.uk/lib/marra.html
  There are further pages for 1701-50 & 1751-1800

Prestonpans
- Prestonpans marriages
  www.ancestor.abel.co.uk/Prestonpans.html
  From the registers of Edinburgh & Inveresk

South Leith
- South Leith Records, compiled from the Parish Registers for the years 1588 to 1700 and from other original sources / D. Robertson (ed.)
  www.scotsfind.org/south_leith/leith.pdf
  Digitised images of edition originally published 1911

Orkney
- Orkney Church Records
  www.genuki.org.uk/big/sct/OKI/churchrec.html
  Primarily notes on the old parish registers

- Orkney Genealogy: Surname Birth/Baptism and Marriage Indices
  www.cursiter.com/pages/indices.htm
  Includes many pages of birth marriage and death records for particular families

Burray
See South Ronaldsay

Firth
See Stenness

Orphir
- Free Church of Scotland Births - Orphir parish 1844, 45, 46.
  http://meg-greenwood.110mb.com/orphir.htm
- Orphir Death Registrations, 1876 - 1880
  http://meg-greenwood.110mb.com/Orphir%20Death%20Registrations%201876-1880.html

South Ronaldsay
- South Ronaldsay and Burray Civil Death Registers: extracted index 1855-1899
  www.southronaldsay.net/cdr
  Also includes some extracts from old parish registers, 1832-44

Stenness
- Free Church of Scotland Births - Firth & Stenness parish, 1846, 1847 & 1848
  http://meg-greenwood.110mb.com/stenness.htm

Peeblesshire

Peebles
- Deaths in Peebles 1874
  http://freepages.genealogy.rootsweb.ancestry.com/~connochie/bdm/peedeaths1874.html

Perthshire
- OPR
  www.npfhg.org/OPRList.pdf
  List of old parish registers for Perthshire

- Cemeteries
  www.genuki.org.uk/big/sct/PER/cemeteries.html
  List of cemetery records held by Perth & Kinross Council in
  Blairgowrie, Crieff, Kinross, Perth and Pitlochry

Fortingall
- Fortingall, Perth: Death Index
  www.npfhg.org/FortingallDeaths.pdf
  Covers 1855-1938

Logierait
- Logierait
  www.npfhg.org/LogieraitBurials.pdf
  Burials 1764-1815

Perth
- Perth Burgh Burial Registers, 1794-1855
  **www.pkc.gov.uk/Education+and+learning/Libraries+archives+and+
  learning+centres/Archives/Archive+collections/Online+sources/
  Perth+burgh+burial+registers.htm**

Renfrewshire
- Births in Renfrew 1866
  **http://freepages.genealogy.rootsweb.ancestry.com/
  ~connochie/bdm/rfwbirths1866.html**
  Continued for 1867 at **/rfwbirths1867.html**

Roxburghshire

Hawick
- Index to James Wilson's Register of Deaths
  www.genuki.org.uk/big/sct/ROX/Hawick/wilson.html
  Solicitor's unofficial register; covers Hawick, 1825-62

Shetland
- Births, Deaths and Marriages in Shetland
  www.users.on.net/~bruce.smith

Stirlingshire

Bothkennar
- Bothkennar Parish Marriages (1723 - 1858)
  http://web.ukonline.co.uk/tom.paterson/census/bothk-mar.html
  Index

Falkirk
- Falkirk Cultural Service Guide to Archives: Cemetery Records
  **www.falkirk.gov.uk/services/community/cultural_services/
  museums/archives/finding_aids/PDFs/cemeteries.pdf**

Larbert
- Larbert Parish Marriages (1760 - 1875)
  http://web.ukonline.co.uk/tom.paterson/census/larb-mar.html
  Index

Muiravonside
- Muiravonside Parish Marriages (1692-1875)
  **http://homepage.ntlworld.com/tom.paterson/census/
  Muiravonside/Muiravon1881_index.htm**

Selkirk
- Deaths in Selkirk 1874
  **http://freepages.genealogy.rootsweb.ancestry.com/
  ~connochie/bdm/seldeaths1874.html**

Stirling
- Deaths in Stirling 1869
  **http://freepages.genealogy.rootsweb.ancestry.com/
  ~connochie/bdm/stideaths1869.html**

Sutherland

Durness
- The Free Church Records of Durness from 18th May 1843 – end
  1855
  www.countysutherland.co.uk/82.html

Rogart

- Births recorded in the Free Church records of Rogart, 1843-1854
  **http://chrisstokes.bravehost.com/ROGART%20FC%
  20BIRTHS%20BY%20DATE.pdf**

West Lothian

- Burial Search
  www.wlfhs.org.uk
  For West Lothian; covers 5 cemeteries to date. Click name

Torphichen

- Register of baptisms, proclamations, marriages and mortcloth dues
  contained in kirk-session records of the parish of Torphichen
  **http://search.ancestry.co.uk/iexec/?htx=BookList&dbid=
  28937&offerid=0%3a7858%3a0**
  Originally published 1911. Pay per view

Wigtownshire

- Old Parish Records (OPR) for Wigtownshire
  **http://freepages.history.rootsweb.ancestry.com/~leighann/
  oprs/intro.html**
- Wigtownshire Death Records: A Brief Explanation
  **http://freepages.history.rootsweb.ancestry.com/~leighann/
  death_records/deaths.html**
- Scottish Parochial Registers: Memoranda of the State of the Parochial
  Registers of Scotland
  www.genuki.org.uk/big/sct/WIG/registers.html
  Report on their condition in Wigtownshire, 1849.
- Wigtownshire BMDs (Births, Marriages & Deaths): an index /
  Grace Stevens
  **http://freepages.history.rootsweb.ancestry.com/~leighann/
  1855/intro.html**
- 1855 Death Records
  **http://freepages.history.rootsweb.ancestry.com/~leighann/
  1855/intro.html**
  In Wigtownshire: the first year of civil registration
- Wigtownshire Free Press Announcements for Births, Marriages, & Deaths
  **http://freepages.history.rootsweb.ancestry.com/~leighann
  wfp/intro.html**

Kirkcolm

- The Wigtownshire Pages: Kirkcolm Old Parish Record Registry
  of the Dead, 1796-1854
  **http://freepages.history.rootsweb.ancestry.com/~leighann
  parishes/kirkcolm/deaths/intro.html**

Kirkmaiden

- The Wigtownshire Pages: Kirkmaiden OPR Death Entries 1779-1854
  **freepages.history.rootsweb.com/~leighann/parishes/
  kirkmaiden/death/intro.html**

Leswalt

- The Wigtownshire Pages: Leswalt OPR Death Entries 1815-1843
  **http://freepages.history.rootsweb.ancestry.com/~leighann/
  parishes/leswalt/death/intro.html**

Old Luce

- Baptisms, Old Luce Parish
  **http://freepages.genealogy.rootsweb.ancestry.com/
  ~wghannay/oldluc e.html**
  Covers 1793-7 (scroll down)

Penninghame

- The Wigtownshire Pages: Old Parish Records, Penninghame Parish
  1695-1820
  **http://freepages.history.rootsweb.ancestry.com/~leighann/
  parishes/penninghame/opr/intro.html**
- From the roll of Baptisms of Penninghame
  **http://freepages.genealogy.rootsweb.ancestry.com/
  ~wghannay/penninghame.html**
  1695-8

Portpatrick

- Portpatrick Death Register 1783-1818
  **http://freepages.history.rootsweb.ancestry.com/~leighann/
  parishes/portpatrick/death/intro.html**

Stoneykirk
- Stoneykirk OPR Death Entries 1778-1797
  http://freepages.history.rootsweb.ancestry.com/~leighann/
  parishes/stoneykirk/death/intro1780.html
- Stoneykirk OPR Death Entries 1839-1854
  http://freepages.history.rootsweb.ancestry.com/~leighann/
  parishes/stoneykirk/death/intro.html

9. The Census

Introductions to the Scottish census are provided by:
- Scotland: Census
  www.genuki.org.uk/big/sct/Census.html not checked
- Family Search Research Wiki: Scotland Census
  https://wiki.familysearch.org/en/Scotland_Census
- Censuses and Quasi-Censuses
  www.scan.org.uk/researchrtools
  Click 'Knowledge Base' and title

Family historians are not the only people interested in census records. For a broader view, see:
- General Register Office for Scotland: Census
  www.gro-scotland.gov.uk/census

The Scotlands People website includes images and indexes of all Scottish censuses, 1841-1901. For an introduction to its census database, visit:
- Scotlands People: Census
  www.scotlandspeople.gov.uk/content/help/index.aspx?r=554&611
  Pay per view site. Includes indexes and images of all censuses, 1841-1901

Ancestry also has images and indexes of Scottish censuses 1841-1901:
- Census & Voter Lists
  http://search.ancestry.co.uk/search/default.aspx?cat=35

There are many other census sites, most of which provide free information. Three gateways are available, although the first one is much the most useful:
- Scotland Census Records
  www.censusfinder.com/scotland.htm
- Census Links: Scotland
  http://censuslinks.com/Scotland
- Census Online: Scotland
  www.census-online.com/links/Scotland

Other important databases include:

- Free CEN Scotland Website
  www.freewebs.com/mmjeffery/index.htm
  Ambitious project to produce free database of all censuses. There are project pages for most counties detailing progress, plus the current searchable database
- Family Search
  www.familysearch.org
  Click 'Search Records' & 'Advanced Search' for online transcript and index of the 1881 census
- Census Films
  www.ktb.net/~dwills/scotref/13311-censusfilms.htm
  List of Latter-Day Saints microfilm of Scottish censuses
- Ayrshire Roots: 1851 Census
  www.ayrshireroots.com/Genealogy/Records/Census/1851/1851.htm
  Includes transcripts for many parishes from most Scottish counties - not just Ayrshire
- Graham Maxwell Ancestry: Free Census Search
  www.maxwellancestry.com/census/default.htm
  Covers much of Southern Scotland for 1841, 1851 and 1861
- Highland Family History Society 1851 Census Index Search
  www.highlandfhs.org.uk/HFHSCensusindexsearchForm.asp
  Covers various parishes in Northern Argyllshire, Caithness, Nairnshire, Ross & Cromarty, and Sutherland
- Terry's Relative Finder: 1841 Census: Invernessshire, Argyllshire, Ross & Cromarty, Bute, Orkney, Caithness, Shetland
  http://freepages.genealogy.rootsweb.ancestry.com/~relys4u
  Collection of extracts
- The Workhouse
  http://users.ox.ac.uk/~peter/workhouse
  Search `Scotland Census' for transcripts of 1881 Census for numerous Scottish workhouses, not otherwise noted below

Aberdeenshire

Aberdeen

- 1851 Partial census - Aberdeenshire, Scotland
  http://genforum.genealogy.com/scotland/messages/#
  34349.html?cj=1&o_xid=0001231185&o_lid=0001231185

Aberdour

- Aberdour: Aberdeenshire 1851 Census
  http://genforum.genealogy.com/scotland/messages/34355.html

Belhelvie

- Belhelvie: Aberdeenshire 1851 Census
  http://Genforum.genealogy.com/scotland/messages/34351.html

Birse

- Census
  http://birsefolk.id.au/census/census_intro.htm
  Census for Birse 1841, Percie & Dalsack 1861, & 1871, and Strahan 1841

Cluny

- Cluny Aberdeenshire 1851 Census
  http://genforum.genealogy.com/scotland/messages/
  34353.html?cj=1&o_xid=0001231185&o_lid=0001231185

Dalsack

See Birse

Glenbuchat

- 1841 Census of Scotland County of Aberdeen, District of Alford, Parish of Glenbucket
  http://members.shaw.ca/doughay/cencglened3-1841.htm
  Continued at **/cencglened2-1841.htm** & **/cencglened3-1841.htm**

King Edward

- King Edward Aberdeenshire 1851 Census
  http://genforum.genealogy.com/scotland/messages/34350.html

Migvie

See Strathdon

Percie

See Birse

Peterhead
- Partial Census for Peterhead, Aberdeenshire, 1851
  **http://genforum.genealogy.com/scotland/
  messages/34347.html?AID=877434&PID=1231185**

Rayne
- Rayne Aberdeenshire 1851 Census
  http://genforum.genealogy.com/scotland/messages/34397.html

Strahan
See Birse

Strathdon
- 1841 Census of the Parish of Strathdon and relevant parts of the Parish
  of Tarland & Migvie
  http://users.tinyonline.co.uk/amchardy/McHardy/1841.htm

Tarland
See Strathdon

Angus
See also Fife
- 1841 Census Index Data - (parts of) Angus, Scotland (also parts of
  Dundee)
  www.monikie.org.uk/1841censusangus.htm

Arbroath
- 1881 Census: Residents of Combination Poor House, Arbroath,
  St Vigeans, Forfar
  www.workhouses.org.uk/index.html?Arbroath/Arbroath1881.shtml

Brechin
- Brechin: Forfarshire 1851 Census
  http://genforum.genealogy.com/scotland/messages/34408.html

Dundee
- Dundee 1851 Census
  http://genforum.genealogy.com/scotland/messages/34411.html

St. Vigeans
- St. Vigeans, Forfarshire 1851 Census
  http://genforum.genealogy.com/scotland/messages/34409.html

Argyll

Colonsay
- Family History Resources for Colonsay & Oransay
  www.colonsay.org.uk/Colonsay%20Records.html
  Includes census pages for 1841-91

Islay
- Islay 1841 Census Records
  http://freepages.history.rootsweb.ancestry.com/~tlarson/index.htm
  For Kilchoman, Kildalton, Kilmeny, Kilarrow, Oa, & Portnahaven
- Islay 1851 Census Records
  http://freepages.misc.rootsweb.ancestry.com/~tlarson/index.htm
  For Kilchoman, Kildalton, Kilmeny, Kilarrow, Oa, and Portnahaven

Kilarrow
See Islay

Kilbrandon
- Kilbrandon and Kilchattan Argyll, Scotland
  http://showcase.netins.net/web/hobbyco/1861.html
  1861 census

Kilchoman
See Islay

Kildalton
See also Islay
- Account of Population in Parish of Kildalton taken in February 1860
  **http://homepages.rootsweb.ancestry.com/~steve/islay/
  rawdata/kild1860.htm**

Kilmeny
See Islay

Muck

- Scottish records on the Web
  www.islemuck.com/census.htm
  Isle of Muck census, 1841-91

Oa
See Islay

Portnahaven
See Islay

Skipness

- 1841 census: Skipness Village, Skipness Parish, Argyllshire Co., Scotland
  www.rootsweb.com/~sctcskip/C1841_village.htm
  For Skipness House, Mill, and Farm, see **/C1841_house.htm**

Ayrshire

- Ayrshire Roots: Census Returns
  www.ayrshireroots.com/Genealogy/Records/Census/Census.htm
- Ayrshire Data from Census OPRs & Kirk Sessions
  www.rootsweb.ancestry.com/~sctayr/census.html
  Many downloadable files
- Ayrshire Ancestors: 1851/61 Ayrshire Census Search Facility
  www.ayrshireancestors.co.uk/search.asp

Newton upon Ayr

- Newton-upon-Ayr: Ayrshire 1851 Census
  http://genforum.genealogy.com/scotland/messages/34352.html

Stevenston

- Stevenston
  www.threetowners.com/Stevenston/stevenston.htm
  Includes information on `censuses' for 1819, 1822, & 1836

Banffshire

Boyndie

- Boyndie: Banffshire 1851 Census
  http://genforum.genealogy.com/scotland/messages/34407.html

Berwickshire

- 1871 Census, Berwick, Scotland
  **http://freepages.genealogy.rootsweb.ancestry.com/
  ~connochie/census/bewcensus1871.html**
  Covers Abbey St. Bathans, Ayton, Bunkle & Preston, Channelkirk, Chirnside, Cockburnspath, Coldingham, Coldstream, Dunse, Earlston, & Eccles

Buteshire

- The Bute 1841 Census
  www.butesonsanddaughters.co.uk/census1841.shtml

Dumfriesshire

- 1851 Census
  www.dgcommunity.net/historicalindexes/census.aspx
  For Dumfriesshire, Kirkcudbrightshire, and Wigtownshire
- Dumfriesshire Census 1851
  **http://homepages.rootsweb.ancestry.com/~scottish/
  DumfriesCensus1851.html**

East Lothian

Aberlady

- 1861 Census Aberlady East Lothian, Scotland
  www.scotlandgenweb.org/readarticle.php?article_id=11

Athelstaneford

- 1861 Census for Athelstaneford, East Lothian, Scotland
  www.scotlandgenweb.org/readarticle.php?article_id=12
  Continued by **id=15** & **id=16**

Dirleton

- 1861 Census, Dirleton, East Lothian, Scotland
  www.scotlandgenweb.org/readarticle.php?article_id=13
  Continued by **id=14**

Dunbar

- Scottish Census Dunbar 1851 2% Census
  www.dwalker.pwp.blueyonder.co.uk/page106.htm

Haddington

- Scottish Census, Haddingtonshire: Haddington 1851 2% census
  www.dwalker.pwp.blueyonder.co.uk/page38.htm

Fife

- Some Fife Born Strays found on the 1851 Census in England
  www.thefifepost.com/censusstraysinengland.htm

Scoonie

- Fife, Scotland: Parish of Scoonie 1841 Census
  http://members.melbpc.org.au/~andes/scoonie.html

Invernessshire

Fort William

- Census, Fort William Area, Inverness-shire, Scotland
  http://freepages.genealogy.rootsweb.ancestry.com/~ked1/ftwillcen.html
  Extracts from 1841, 1861 & 1881

Glenmoriston

See Urquhart

Muck

- Scottish Research on the Web
  www.islemuck.com/census.htm
  Transcripts of Isle of Muck censuses 1841-91

North Uist

- 1841 North Uist Census
  http://freepages.genealogy.rootsweb.ancestry.com/~ked1/
  1841NorthUist.html

Urquhart

- 1881 Census of Urquhart & Glenmoriston
  www.angelfire.com/ak2/akeddy/census2.html

Kincardineshire

Kincardine

- 1841 Census, Kincardine, Scotland: Introduction
  http://freepages.genealogy.rootsweb.ancestry.com/
  ~connochie/kcd/1841kcdintro.html

Kinrossshire

- 1841 Census of Kinross
  http://member.melbpc.org.au/~andes/scotland
  Includes transcripts and indexes for Arngask, Cleish, Forgandenny, Fossoway & Tulliebole, and Portmoak

Kirkcudbrightshire

See also Dumfriesshire, & Wigtownshire

Buittle

- Buittle Census Returns 1841, 1851, 1861 & 1881
  www.buittle.org.uk/census.htm

Lanarkshire

- Indexes to 1851 census of Lanarkshire outwith Glasgow
  www.desgarrity.co.uk/51c.html
  Details of fiche indexes
- Indexes to the 1861 census returns of the Registration Districts of Lanarkshire
  www.desgarrity.co.uk/61c.html
  Details of a CD

Dalserf

- Parish of Dalserf
  www.scottap.com/family/Lanark/Census1841Dalserf.html
  1841 Census

Midlothian

Duddingston

- Scottish Census: Duddingston, Edinburgh 1851 2% census
  www.dwalker.pwp.blueyonder.co.uk/page37.htm

Edinburgh

- Edinburgh St Cuthberts
  http://freepages.genealogy.rootsweb.ancestry.com/~agene/
  census/edstcuthberts.htm

  Extracts for 1851

Lasswade
- Scottish Census: Midlothian, Lasswade 1851 2% census
  www.dwalker.pwp.blueyonder.co.uk/page105.htm

Orkney
Burray
See South Ronaldsay

Egilsay
See Rousay

Eynhallow
See Rousay

Papa Westray
- Papa Westray census 1841
  www.btinternet.com/~alan.price/papay/pwcensus1841.htm
  Includes a separate page for 1851 census

Rousay
- Censuses of Rousay, Egilsay, Wyre, & Eynhallow
  www.rousayroots.com/censuses.html

Sanday
- 1841 Sanday, Orkney Census
  www.cursiter.com/txt-exe-files/Cen41.txt

South Ronaldsay
- South Ronaldsay and Burray 1821 Census Project
  www.southronaldsay.net/1821

Wyre
See Rousay

Perthshire
Dunning
- Parish of Dunning Census Records
  www.dunning.uk.net/census.html

Fortingall
- 1881 Census: Fortingall, Perth, Scotland
  www.npfhg.org/Fortingall1881.pdf

Kirkmichael
- 1851 Census: Kirkmichael
  www.npfhg.org/Kirkmichael1851Census.pdf
- 1891 Census for Kirkmichael Perthshire
  www.npfhg.org/Kirkmichael1891Census.pdf
- 1901
  www.npfhg.org/Kirkmichael1901Census.pdf
  Kirkmichael census

Ross & Cromarty
Achiltibuie
- Achiltibuie : Transcripts and Notes
  http://freepages.genealogy.rootsweb.ancestry.com/~coigach/achil.htm
  Includes census transcriptions

Altandhu
- Altandhu
  http://freepages.genealogy.rootsweb.ancestry.com/~coigach/
  altandhu.htm
  Includes censuses, 1841-91

Badenscallie
- Notes on Badenscallie
  http://freepages.genealogy.rootsweb.ancestry.com/~coigach/nbadsc.htm
  Includes census transcriptions

Camusglassellan
See Reiff

Coigach
- Coigach Annotated Census
  http://freepages.genealogy.rootsweb.ancestry.com/~coigach/nother.htm
  Extracts 1841-91

Cromarty
- Cromarty Courthouse Museum: List of householders in Cromarty, 1744
  www.cali.co.uk/users/freeway/courthouse/geneal2.html

Faochag
See Reiff

Lochbroom
See Altandhu & Reiff

Reiff
- Notes for Reiff, Camusglassellan & Faochag
  http://freepages.genealogy.rootsweb.ancestry.com/~coigach/reff.htm
  Includes censuses, 1841-91

Rosemarkie
- 1891 Census, Rosemarkie, Ross & Cromarty, Scotland
  http://freepages.genealogy.rootsweb.ancestry.com/~connochie/census/rosemarkiecensus1891.html

Tain
- 1851 Census, Tain, Ross & Cromarty, Scotland: Partial Transcriptions
  http://freepages.genealogy.rootsweb.ancestry.com/~connochie/census/taincensus1851.html
  For 1891, see **/taincensus1891.html**

Tanera
- The Isle Tanera
  http://freepages.genealogy.rootsweb.ancestry.com/~coigach/tanera.htm
  Includes census transcriptions

Shetland

Foula
- Isle of Foula, Shetland 1841 & 1851 Censuses
  http://uk-transcriptions.accessgenealogy.com/Foula,1841%20&%201851.htm
  Also pages for 1861, 1871 & 1891

Stirlingshire
- Stirlingshire Records
  http://web.ukonline.co.uk/tom.paterson/census/larb_both_index.htm
  Census records, *etc.*, for various parishes

Airth
- Airth 1881 Census
  web.ukonline.co.uk/tom.paterson/census/Airth/Airth1881_index.html

Banton
- Banton (Engine, Mallion, and Auchinmully Villages) - 1851 Census
  www.paperclip.org.uk/kilsythweb/history/archivesources/kilsyth_scotland_1851_census.htm

Bothkennar
- Bothkennar Census 1851
  http://web.ukonline.co.uk/tom.paterson/census/bothkind.htm
- Bothkennar 1881 census Surname Index
  http://homepage.ntlworld.com/tomp.paterson/census/Bothkennar/Bothk1881_index.htm

Denny
- Denny 1881 Census
  www.tompaterson.co.uk/census/Denny/Denny1881_index.html

Dunipace
- Dunipace 1881 Census
  http://web.ukonline.co.uk/tom.paterson/census/Dunipace/Dunipace1881_index.html

Falkirk
- Falkirk Burgh - 1881 Census
  www.tompaterson.co.uk/census/Falkirk/FalkirkB1881_index.html
- Falkirk Landward - 1881 Census
  www.tompaterson.co.uk/census/FalkirkL/FalkirkL1881_index.html

Larbert
- Larbert 1851 Census - Index to Place Names
  http://web.ukonline.co.uk/tom.paterson/census/larbert1851_loc_index.html

- Larbert 1881 Census
  http://homepage.ntlworld.com/tom.paterson/census/
  larbert1881_index.htm

Muiravonside
- Muiravonside 1881 Census
  http://homepage.ntlworld.com/tomp.paterson/census/
  Muiravonside/Muiravon1881_index.htm

Polmont
- Polmont 1881 Census - Index
  http://web.ukonline.co.uk/members/tom.paterson/census/
  Polmont/Polmont1881_index.html

St. Ninians
- St. Ninians 1881 Census
  http://web.ukonline.co.uk/tom.paterson/census/StNinians/
  StNinians1881_index.html

Slamannan
- Slamannan 1881 Census
  www.tompaterson.co.uk/census/Slamannan/Slam1881_index.html

Sutherland
Golspie
- Golspie Census 1811
  www.countysutherland.co.uk/49.html
- Census of the Inhabitants on Culmaily, Golspie, 1810, taken from Sutherland Estate Management Papers
  www.countysutherland.co.uk/60.html

West Lothian
- 1851 Census Search
  www.wlfhs.org.uk
  For West Lothian. Click name
- 1901 Census Search
  www.wlfhs.org.uk
  For West Lothian. Click name

Uphall
- Uphall on the Web: 1841 Census
  www.uphall.org/index.php?option=com_content&view=
  article&id=123&Itemid=135
- Uphall on the Web: 1851 Census
  www.uphall.org/index.php?option=com_content&view=
  article&id=124&Itemid=136

Wigtownshire
See also Dumfriesshire
- The Wigtownshire Pages: Wigtownshire Census Records
  http://freepages.history.rootsweb.ancestry.com/~leighann/
  census/intro.html
  General discussion
- The Wigtownshire Pages: Parish Lists of Wigtownshire and Minnigaff, 1684
  http://freepages.history.rootsweb.ancestry.com/~leighann/
  1684/intro.html
  Transcript of a book published in 1916. Minnigaff is in Kirkcudbrightshire
- Heads of Household, 1851 Census Wigtownshire Parishes John Roy's Index of Heads of Family
  http://freepages.history.rootsweb.ancestry.com/~leighann/
  parishes /51_census/census_info.html
  Includes pages for Glasserton, Inch, Kirkcolm, Kirkcowan, Kirkinner, Kirkmaiden, Leswalt, Leswalt/Stranraer, Mochrum, New Luce, Old Luce/Glenluce, Penninghame, Portpatrick,Sorbie, Stoneykirk, Stranraer, Whithorn, & Wigtown

Portpatrick
- The Wigtownshire Pages: Urquhart Census of Portpatrick
  http://freepages.history.rootsweb.ancestry.com/~leighann/
  census/urquhart.html
  Ecclesiastical censuses taken 1832-54

Sorbie
- Wigtownshire Census 1851: Sorbie
  http://homepages.rootsweb.ancestry.com/~scottish/
  WigtonCensus1851.html

10. Monumental Inscriptions

Introduction
- Researching Your Graveyard
  www.scottishgraveyards.org.uk/downloads/1researching.pdf

Gateway
- Scotlands Family: Deaths, Burial Records and Monumental Inscriptions
  www.scotlandsfamily.com/deaths.htm

Collections & General
- Family Search Research Wiki: Scotland Cemeteries
  https://wiki.familysearch.org/en/Scotland_Cemeteries
- Scottish Graveyards
  www.scottishgraveyards.org.uk/index.shtml
- Find a Grave: Scotland
  www.findagrave.com
  Click on 'Browse by location' and 'Scotland'. Lists graves of 224 famous Scots
- Interment.net: Scottish Cemeteries
  http://interment.net/uk/scot/index.htm
- Family History: Index of Published Monumental Inscriptions
  www.nls.uk/family-history/gravestones/inscriptions/index.cfm
  In the National Library of Scotland
- Monumental Inscriptions in the Mitchell Library
  www.glasgow.gov.uk/NR/rdonlyres/CD3FE900-C0E9-48F0-8FCA-5B1D481C0970/0/Monumental_Inscriptions_Oct07.pdf
  Extensive listing of published inscriptions
- Full text of 'Inscriptions on the tombstones and monuments erected in memory of the Covenanters [microform] with historical introd. and notes'
  www.archive.org/stream/MN5159ucmf_10/MN5159ucmf_10_djvu.txt
- Full text of 'Monuments and monumental inscriptions in Scotland'
  www.archive.org/stream/monumentsmonumen01rogeiala/monumentsmonumen01rogeiala_djvu.txt

- Jewish Cemeteries in Scotland
  www.jgsgb.org.uk/bury03.shtml
- Monumental Inscriptions Index of Places
  www.scotlandspeoplehub.gov.uk/pdf/monumental%20inscriptions.pdf
- Scottish Monumental Inscriptions
  http://scottishmis.homestead.com/
  Details of inscriptions available on CD
- Scottish-American Gravestones, 1700-1900 / David Dobson
  http://search.ancestry.co.uk/iexec/?htx=BookList&dbid=49333&offerid=0%3a7858%3a0
  Originally published Genealogical Publishing Co., 2003

Brasses
- Scotland
  www.mbs-brasses.co.uk/page183.html
  Bibliography of monumental brasses

Aberdeenshire
- Index to Memorial Inscriptions
  www.abdnet.co.uk/mi-index
  Covering many kirkyards in Aberdeenshire, Banffshire, Kincardineshire and Moray
- Burial grounds in North-East Scotland
  www.abdnet.co.uk/burialgrounds
  Map
- Aberdeenshire Graveyards
  http://myweb.tiscali.co.uk/nescotland/graveyards/grabdnshr.htm
  Photographs of headstones

Aberdeen
- Aberdeen City Graveyards and Cemeteries
  http://myweb.tiscali.co.uk/nescotland/graveyards/grabdncty.htm

Birse
- Birse Kirkyard
  http://birsefolk.id.au/birse_kirkyard%20-%20New.htm

Angus
- Angus Council: Burial Grounds
  www.angus.gov.uk/services/view_service_detail.cfm?serviceid=1186

Broughty Ferry
- Old Burial Ground at Broughty Ferry, Dundee, Scotland
  www.monikie.org.uk/bf-oldburialground.htm

Dundee
- Dundee City Council: Maps of the City's Cemeteries
  www.dundeecity.gov.uk/leisurecomms/cemeterymaps
- The Howff Graveyard
  www.fdca.org.uk/FDCAHowffInfo.html
  At Dundee

Monikie
- Memorial Inscriptions and Photographs of the Older Gravestones situated in the Kirkyard of Monikie parish Kirk, Angus
  www.monikie.org.uk/kirkyard.htm
- The Old Memorials at the Graves in Monikie Kirkyard, in Angus, Scotland
  www.monikie.org.uk/monkirkgraves.htm

Argyll
See also Sutherland

Colonsay
- Colonsay Graveyard
  www.colonsay.org.uk/COLRIPweb.pdf

Islay
- Isle of Islay Cemetery Database
  http://homepages.rootsweb.ancestry.com/~steve/islay/cemetery

Skipness
- Skipness Monumental Inscriptions from Kilbrannan Chapel (also known as St. Brendan's and Skipness Chapel)
  www.rootsweb.ancestry.com/~sctcskip/mi.htm
  Continued at **/mi2.htm**

Southend
- Kilcolmkeil Churchyard: Southend Parish, Kintyre Peninsula, Argyll, Scotland
  www.ralstongenealogy.com/keilchurchyard.php

Ayrshire
- Ayrshire Roots: Monumental Inscriptions
  www.ayrshireroots.com/Genealogy/Records/MIs/MIs.htm
  Includes transcripts from many churchyards and cemeteries
- Ayrshire Ancestors On-Line Cemetery Search
  www.ayrshireancestors.co.uk/CemeteryHome.htm
  Inscriptions database
- Graves and burial records of North Ayrshire and Arran
  www.ayrshireroots.com/Genealogy/Records/Burial/Burial%20Grounds%20in%20Ayrshire.htm
- [Ayrshire Headstones (mostly)]
  http://web.archive.org/web/20041126160313/www.headstones.freeserve.co.uk
  Lists of headstones at Ardrossan, Arran, Ayr, Dalry, Dreghorn, Dundonald, Galston, Glasgow, Irvine, Kilbirnie, Kilmarnock, Kilwinning, Mauchline, Monkton, Newmilns, Saltcoats, Stevenston, Stewarton, Tarbolton, Troon, and West Kilbride

Ardrossan
- Ardrossan Cemetery, Ardrossan, North Ayrshire, Scotland
  www.interment.net/data/scotland/n_ayrsh/ardrossan/index.htm

Carrick
- Monumental Inscriptions for Carrick, Ayrshire
  www.maybole.org/history/books/monumentinscriptions/carrick.htm

Dalrymple
- Deaths in Dalrymple Parish
  www.geographyhigh.connectfree.co.uk/familyhistorydalrympledea.html
  Gravestone inscriptions

Fenwick
- Some Fenwick Churchyard Monumental Inscriptions
  www.ayrshireroots.com/Towns/Fenwick/Fenwick%20MIs.htm

Kirkbride
- Kirkbride Kirkyard
  www.maybole.org/history/Archives/Kirkbride/Kirkyard.htm

Maybole
- The Monumental Inscriptions in Maybole Old Parish Kirkyard
  www.maybole.org/history/Archives/Kirkwynd/kirkwynd.htm

Ochiltree

- Index to Headstones
  http://ochiltreechurch.homestead.com/Headstones.html
  At Ochiltree

Stair

- Cemetery Headstone Index: Stair
  http://stairchurch.homestead.com/Headstones.html

Stevenson

- Hawkhill Cemetery, Stevenson, North Ayrshire, Scotland
  www.interment.net/data/scotland/n_ayrsh/hawkhill/index.htm

Stevenston

- Stevenston Monumental Inscriptions
  www.ayrshireroots.com/Towns/Stevenston/Stevenston%20MIs.htm
- Monumental Inscriptions Stevenston High Kirk / Mairi Frew (ed)
  www.threetowners.com/Stevenston/burials.htm

Banffshire

See also Aberdeenshire

Banff

- Annals of Banff Index to the Old Cemetery
  http://gen.deltanz.net/banff/banffindex.html

Berwickshire

- Borders Family History Society Gravestones Index
  www.bordersfhs.org.uk/BFHSGravestoneIndexSearch.asp
  For Berwickshire, Peeblesshire, Roxburghshire & Selkirkshire
- Berwickshire Graveyards: their location
  www.rootsweb.ancestry.com/~sctbew/Cemeteries/cemindex.htm
- Berwick & Roxburgh Monumental Inscriptions
  www.hogarth.org.uk/scotref1.htm
  Actually covers a number of burial grounds in the two counties

Whitsome

- The Old Burial Ground
  http://homepages.ipact.nl/~robertson/whitsome%201%
  20place%20study/burial_ground/index.html
  At Whitsome

Buteshire

- Headstones Buteshire
  www.members.shaw.ca/Buteshire/headstones_buteshire.htm
  Details submitted by users

Caithness

See also Sutherland

- Caithness Cemeteries pre-1855 Tombstone Inscriptions
  http://homepages.rootsweb.com/~mwi/caithness.txt
- Burial Grounds of Caithness and Sutherland / A. S. Cowper
  www.caithness.org/atoz/cemeteries/
  burialgroundscaithnesssusutherland.htm

Dumfriesshire

- Churches and Graveyards in Dumfries and Galloway
  homepages.rootsweb.ancestry.com/~dfsgal
  Photographs only
- [Some Gravestones Inscriptions from Dumfries-Galloway]
  http://homepages.rootsweb.ancestry.com/~scottish/D-GInscriptions.html
  Inscriptions from c.50 graveyards
- Cemetery Index Scotland
  www.johnmacmillan.co.uk/indx_cemetery.html
  Includes inscriptions from cemeteries at Annan, Cummertrees, Ecclefechan, Hoddom Cross, St. Kentigern's Graveyard, Lochmaben, Mouswald, Rigg, Ruthwell, Tinwald, and Torthorwald.
- Dumfries born, Foreign Buried
  http://homepages.rootsweb.ancestry.com/~scottish/
  D-GForeignBurie.html?

Dunbartonshire

Roseneath

- Old Graveyard, Roseneath, Dunbartonshire
  http://members.madasafish.com/~fairenough/
  Monumental Inscriptions

East Lothian

Bolton

- Monumental Inscriptions
  www.ndhm.org.uk/page_5.htm
  For Bolton, Saltoun, and Pencaitland

Haddington
- St. Mary's Parish Church, Haddington: The Graveyard Index and Plan
  www.stmaryskirk.com/6_graveyard_index_plan.htm
  Monumental Inscriptions

Pencaitland
See Bolton

Prestonkirk
See Traprain

Saltoun
See Bolton

Stenton
See Traprain

Traprain
- Evan Clarke's Web Site
  www.ejclark.force9.co.uk
  Includes burial ground surveys for Prestonkirk, Stenton, & Whittingehame

Whittinghame
See Traprain

Fife
- Cemeteries in Fife
  www.genuki.org.uk:8080/big/sct/FIF/Cemeteries.htm
  List
- Cemeteries and Churchyard Records in Fife: where can I find them?
  www.thefifepost.com/cemeteries.htm

Carnbee
- Some Monuments in Carnbee Kirkyard in Fife
  www.ancestor.abel.co.uk/Carnbee.html

Tulliallan
- The Restoration of Tulliallan Kirkyard
  www.rocinante.demon.co.uk/klhg/tullkirk/tullindx.htm

Invernessshire
See also Sutherland

Boleskine
- Boleskine Cemetery, Scotland
  www.pharmcat.demon.co.uk/cemetery/boleskine/boleskine.htm
  Photographs

Corrimony
- Corrimony Cemetery
  http://freepages.genealogy.rootsweb.ancestry.com/~ked1/Glen9f.html

Glenurquhart & Glenmoriston
- Glenurquhart & Glenmoriston Cemetery Inscriptions
  http://freepages.genealogy.rootsweb.ancestry.com/~ked1/Glen9.html
  From Clachan An Inbhir, Corrimony, Dalchriechart, Daviot, Kilmartin, and Kilmore

Inverness
- Chapel Yard Cemetery, Inverness
  www.pharmcat.demon.co.uk/cemetery/chapel
  Photographs

Tomnahurich
- Tomnahurich Cemetery, Inverness, Scotland
  www.pharmcat.demon.co.uk/cemetery/thurich/index.htm
  Photographs

Kincardineshire
See also Aberdeenshire
- Kincardineshire Graveyards
  http://myweb.tiscali.co.uk/nescotland/graveyards/grkincd.htm
  Photographs of headstones

Kirkcudbrightshire
- Cemetery Index Scotland
  www.johnmacmillan.co.uk/indx_cemetery.html
  Includes pages for cemeteries at Balmaghie, Buittle, Castle Douglas, Corsock, Crossmichael, Dalbeattie, Kelton, Kirkgunzeon, Kirkpatrick-Durham, Lochrutton, Parton, & Urr.

Buittle

- The Churchyards of the Stewartry: Buittle / J. Matthewson
  www.buittle.org.uk/churchyard.htm

Crossmichael

- Saint Michael Churchyard, Dumfries and Galloway County, Scotland
  www.interment.net/data/scotland/dumf_gall/stmike/michael.htm
  At Crossmichael, Kirkcudbrightshire

Lanarkshire

- Cemeteries and Crematoria in North Lanarkshire
  www.genuki.org.uk/big/sct/LKS/cemeteries-nl.htm
  List
- Cemeteries and Crematoria in South Lanarkshire
  www.genuki.org.uk/big/sct/LKS/cemeteries-sl.htm
  List

Cambuslang

- Cambuslang Parish: Memorial Inscriptions 1722-1854
  http://web.archive.org/web/20070808132015/
  www.heather5.com/cambusmi.html

Glasgow

- Cemeteries and Crematoria in Glasgow
  www.genuki.org.uk/big/sct/LKS/cemeteries-gla.html
  List
- Southern Necropolis Research
  www.southernnecropolis.com
  Glasgow cemetery. See also:
- Southern Necropolis Research
  www.southernnec.20m.com

Larkhall

- Larkhall Cemetery Lair Owners Wallchart
  http://scots-roots.homestead.com/LarkhallCemeteryLairOwners.html

Motherwell

- Saint Patrick Churchyard, Motherwell, North Lanarkshire County, Scotland
  www.interment.net/data/scotland/no_lanark/stpat/index.htm

Strathaven

- Strathaven Cemetery M.I's
  http://freepages.genealogy.rootsweb.ancestry.com/~barrieMidlothian
- Visit Midlothian Stones
  www.edinburgh.org/downloads/midlothian-stones.pdf

Corstorphine

- Parish of Corstorphine
  www.angelfire.com/ct2/corstorphine
  Includes five-page index of Corstorphine inscriptions

Edinburgh

- Edinburgh graves for the family historian
  www.edinburgh.gov.uk/internet/Leisure/Libraries/
  Explore_your_library/Family_history/CEC_edinburgh_
  graves_for_the_family_historian
  Guidance notes from the Edinburgh Room
- Edinburgh Ancestors
  www.edinburghancestors.org.uk
  Monumental inscriptions database
- Rosebank Cemetery, Pilrig Street, Edinburgh: Inscriptions of Tombstones in Rosebank cemetery
  www.dwalker.pwp.blueyonder.co.uk/Cemeteries/
  Rosebank%20Cemetery.htm
- Monumental Inscriptions in St. Cuthbert's Churchyard, Edinburgh [Older Portion]
  www.scotsfind.org/st.cuthbert's_access/St.Cuthbert's.pdf
  Originally published Scottish Record Society, 1915

Inveresk

- Monumental Inscriptions in Inveresk Kirkyard extant in 1857
  www.ancestor.abel.co.uk/inv/mi1857.html

Moray

- The Moray Burial Ground Research Group
  www.mbgrg.org
  Includes index to 29,500 names

Nairnshire
See Sutherland

Orkney

Brinian
- Brinian Kirkyard
  www.genuki.org.uk/big/sct/OKI/Rousay/brinian.html

Egilsay
- Egilsay Kirkyard
  www.genuki.org.uk/big/sct/OKI/Rousay/egilsay.html

Glebe
- Glebe Kirkyard
  www.genuki.org.uk/big/sct/OKI/Rousay/glebe.html

Scockness
- Scockness Kirkyard
  www.genuki.org.uk/big/sct/OKI/Rousay/scocknes.html

Wasbister
- Wasbister Kirkyard
  www.genuki.org.uk/big/sct/OKI/Rousay/wasbistr.html

Westside
- Westside Kirkyard
  www.genuki.org.uk/big/sct/OKI/Rousay/westside.html

Wyre
- Wyre Kirkyard
  www.genuki.org.uk/big/sct/OKI/Rousay/wyre.html

Peeblesshire
See Berwickshire

Perthshire

Callander
- Monumental Inscriptions at Little Leny, Callander
  www.incallander.co.uk/lit_len.htm

Dunning
- Dunning St. Serf's Church Grave Yard Survey
  www.dunning.uk.net/gstart.html

Perth
- Wellshill Cemetery, Perth: Register of the Polish Casualties
  www.ostrycharz.free-online.co.uk/WellshillRegister.html

Renfrewshire
- Gravestones
  www.owkgreenock.info
  At the Old West Kirk, Greenock. Click title

Ross & Cromarty
See also Sutherland

Fearn Peninsula
- Graveyard Project
  www.fearnpeninsulagraveyards.com/Home.html
  Covers 8 cemeteries in the Fearn Peninsula area.

Roxburghshire
See also Berwickshire

Abbotsrule
- Abbotrule Churchyard: list of surnames
  www.genuki.org.uk/big/sct/ROX/Abbotrule/gravelist.html

Ashkirk
- Ashkirk Churchyard: list of surnames
  www.genuki.org.uk/big/sct/ROX/Ashkirk/gravelist.html

Borthwick
- Borthwick Wa's Churchyard: list of surnames
  www.genuki.org.uk/big/sct/ROX/Roberton/gravelistB.html

Cavers
- Cavers Old Churchyard list of surnames
  www.genuki.org.uk/big/sct/ROX/Cavers/gravelist.html

Roberton

- Roberton Parish Burial Ground: list of surnames
  www.genuki.org.uk/big/sct/ROX/Roberton/gravelistR.html

Selkirkshire

See also Berwickshire

Ettrick

- Ettrick Churchyard: List of Surnames
  www.genuki.org.uk/big/sct/SEL/Ettrick/gravelist.html*Gala Aisle*
- Gala Aisle Cemetery
  www.scotlandgenweb.org/selkirkshire/aisle/aisle.htm

Galashiels

- Eastlands Cemetery, Galashiels, Borders County, Scotland
  www.interment.net/data/scotland/borders/eastlands/index.htm

Stirlingshire

Falkirk

- Camelon Cemetery, Falkirk, Stirlingshire County, Scotland
  www.interment.net/data/scotland/stirling/camelon/index.htm

Gargunnock

- List of Surnames in Gargunnock Churchyard Inscriptions
  www.mclarn.plus.com/page5.html
  Scroll down to bottom of page

Kilsyth

- Pre 1855 Inscriptions Kilsyth Old Churchyard
  **www.paperclip.org.uk/kilsythweb/history/
  archivesources/pre_1855_inscriptions.htm**
- Memorial Inscriptions from Kilsyth Old Churchyard Stirling
  shire, Scotland
  http://members.tripod.com/~Caryl_Williams/Kilsyth-7.html

Yarrow

- Yarrow Churchyard: List of Surnames
  www.genuki.org.uk/big/sct/SEL/Yarrow/gravelistY.html

- St. Mary's Kirkyard: List of Surnames
  www.genuki.org.uk/big/sct/SEL/Yarrow/gravelistS.html
  In Yarrow

Shetland

- Headstones
  **http://bayanne.info/Shetland/browsemedia.php?
  mediatypeID=headstones**
  In Shetland

Sutherland

See also Caithness

- The Burial Grounds of Sutherland
  www.countysutherland.co.uk/11.html
- Highland Family History Society: Gravestones Index Search
  www.highlandfhs.org.uk/HFHSGravestoneIndexSearch.asp
  Covers Caithness, Invernessshire, Ross & Cromarty, Nairnshire,
  Sutherland, and parts of Argyll
- Burial Grounds of Sutherland
  www.countysutherland.co.uk/11.html
  Database with many photographs

Wigtownshire

- The Wigtownshire Pages: Graveyards / Jim Mclay
  **http://freepages.history.rootsweb.ancestry.com/~leighann/
  articles/history/graveyards.html**
- The Wigtownshire Pages: Monumental Inscriptions /
  J.E. Birchman
  **http://freepages.history.rootsweb.ancestry.com/~leighann/
  chapple/mi2.html**
  Surname index for Cruggleton (with Kirkmadrine), Kirkinner,
  Penninghame, Sorbie, and Whithorn

Whithorn

- Monumental Inscriptions: St. Ninian's Old Churchyard,
  Whithorn, Wigtownshire, Scotland
  **http://homepages.rootsweb.ancestry.com/~scottish/
  indexstninian2.html**

11. Other Sources

The civil registers, old parish registers, monumental inscriptions, and census records are all vital sources for family historians. But a wide range of web-based information on other sources is also available. This includes much useful advice; it also includes an increasing amount of actual data. A gateway is provided by:

- UK GDL: UK Genealogical Directories and Lists on the Internet
  www.ukgdl.org.uk

For a general introduction to sources, consult:
- Interpreting Scottish Records / Diane Baptie
  www.ayrshireroots.com/Genealogy/Records/Legal%20Records.htm

For an introduction intended for local historians, see:
- Scotland's Rural Past: Historic Documents
  www.scotlandsruralpast.org.uk/index.php?option=com_
  content&task=view&id=35&Itemid=51

Many useful leaflets are available on two sites:
- National Archives of Scotland: Guides
  www.nas.gov.uk/guides/default.asp
- Scottish Archive Network: Research Tools
  www.scan.org.uk/researchrtools

Many examples of documents can be viewed at:
- Scottish Archive Network: Virtual Vault
  www.scan.org.uk/researchrtools/virtualvault.htm

For a general introduction to the records of Scottish government, see:
- Scottish Government Records after 1707
  www.nas.gov.uk/guides/scottishGovernmentAfter1707.asp

A number of sites offer important collections of databases. These include:
- Ancestry.co.uk Scotland Historical Records
  www.ancestry.co.uk/search/locality/dbpage.aspx?tp=3257&p=3252

- Scottish Genealogy Databases
  www.scotsfind.org
- Scots Origins
  www.scotsorigins.com
  Includes the I.G.I. (International Genealogical Index)., also permits ordering of census and old parish register/civil register transcripts
- Historical Indexes
  www.dgcommunity.net/historicalindexes/default.aspx
  Collection of databases relating to Dumfriesshire, Kirkcudbright-shire and Wigtownshire
- World Vital Records
  www.worldvitalrecords.com/contentlisting.aspx
  Collection of international databases, including some relating to Scotland

Aliens Registers
- Registers of Aliens
  www.edinburgh.gov.uk/internet/Attachments/Internet/
  Council/Council_Business/City_archives/Collections%
  20and%20indexes/Aliens%20Book%20Index.pdf
  For 1793-1825

Burgh Records
See Municipal and Parochial Records

Business Records

Stirlingshire
- Finding Aids for Archives: Business
  www.falkirk.gov.uk/services/community/cultural_services/
  museums/archives/finding_aids/business_a_to_z.aspx
  In Falkirk Archives

Chancery Records
- National Archives of Scotland: The Chancery pre-1707
  www.nas.gov.uk/guides/chancery.asp

Church Records
See also Quaker Records & Roman Catholic Records

Scotland: Church Records
www.genuki.org.uk/big/sct/ChurchRecords.html
Scotland, Church of; Records of the General Assembly
www.british-history.ac.uk/place.aspx?gid=115&region=7
From the printed calendars for 1560-1842
National Archives of Scotland: Commissary Court Records
www.nas.gov.uk/guides/commissaryCourt.asp
Guide to ecclesiastical courts
- The Scottish Kirk Session / Robin Fairservice
http://members.tripod.com/~pg_genealogy_society/kirk_session.htm
General discussion
- Kirk Session and Other Material found in the Old Parochial Registers
www.scotlandspeoplehub.gov.uk/pdf/list-of-oprs-appendix2.pdf
Calendar of records
- Church Records
www.scotsgenealogy.com/online/church_records.pdf

Aberdeenshire
- Index to *The Presbytery Book of Strathbogie, 1631-1654*
www.kinhelp.co.uk/KinHelp/genealogical-indices/gene14

Angus
- Heads of Families in the Parish of Glamis in Communion with the Church of Scotland, December 1834.
www.genuki.org.uk:8080/big/sct/ANS/Glamis/289phf.html
- Kirkoswald Kirk Session Records
www.maybole.org/community/kirkoswald/
kirkoswaldkirksessionrecords.htm

Dumfriesshire
- Dumfries Kirk Session
www.dgcommunity.net/historicalindexes/dfskirksession.aspx
For 1689-1838; also Presbytery records 1687-95
- Mouswald Kirk Session Minutes 1640-1659
www.dgcommunity.net/historicalindexes/mwlkirksession.aspx

Fife
- Synod and Presbytery Records: Fife
www.genuki.org.uk/big/sct/FIF/Synod.htm
Locations

- The Presbyterie Booke of Kirkcaldie, being the record of that presbytery from the 15th day of April 1630 to the 14th day of September 1653
www.scotsfind.org/kirkcaldy_access/kirkcaldie.pdf
Digitised images of a book originally published by James Burt, 1900

Kirkcudbrightshire
- Troqueer Kirk Sessions Minutes
www.dgcommunity.net/historicalindexes/trqkirksession.aspx
For 1698-1771

Lanarkshire
- Cambusnethan Parish Communion Roll 1640
www.scottap.com/family/Lanark/Cambusnethan1640.html
- Kilsyth Heritors' Minutes (transcripts) 1813-1844, North Lanarkshire Council Archives (UK1/4/1)
www.scan.org.uk/researchrtools/heritors.htm

Midlothian
- The Commissariat of Edinburgh Consistorial Processes and Decreets 1658-1800
www.scotsfind.org/processes_access/processes.pdf
Published by the Scottish Record Society, 1909. Calendar of ecclesiastical court proceedings

Orkney
- North Ronaldsay Free Kirk Session Records
http://meg-greenwood.110mb.com/session2.htm
- Orphir Free Kirk Session Records, 1844-1900
http://meg-greenwood.110mb.com/session.htm
- Stromness Free Church Session records beginning 1844
http://meg-greenwood.110mb.com/stromness.htm

Stirlingshire
- Finding Aids for Archives: Churches
www.falkirk.gov.uk/services/community/cultural_services/
museums/archives/finding_aids/churches.aspx
Records held in Falkirk Archives

Sutherland
- County Sutherland: Golspie People 1752
  www.countysutherland.co.uk/26.html
  List of seat holders in the church
- Rogart Free Church
  www.countysutherland.co.uk/86.html

Wigtownshire
- Stoneykirk, Wigtownshire, Kirk Session Minutes, 1886-1902
  http://meg-greenwood.110mb.com/wigtown.html

Court Records
- Family Search Research Wiki: Scotland Court Records
  https://wiki.familysearch.org/en/Scotland_Court_Records
- National Archives of Scotland: Court of Session: Introduction to Processes
  www.nas.gov.uk/guides/introductionToProcesses.asp
- National Archives of Scotland: Court of Session: Unextracted Processes
  www.nas.gov.uk/guides/unextractedProcesses.asp
  Further guides to 'extracted processes after 1660', 'Other Court of Session series', and 'Sequestrations' can be accessed from this page
- Virtual Vault: Court Records
  www.scan.org.uk/researchrtools/courtrecords.htm

Customs & Excise Records
- National Archives of Scotland: Customs and Excise Records
  www.nas.gov.uk/guides/customs.asp

Directories
- Postal Directories
  www.scan.org.uk/knowledgebase/topics/postaldirectories_topic.htm
- Family Relatives
  www.familyrelatives.co.uk
  Includes a substantial collection of Scottish trade directories. Pay per view

- U.K City and County Directories, 1600s-1900s
  http://search.ancestry.co.uk/Browse/list.aspx?dbid=1547&path=Scotland
  Includes 8 Scottish directories, 1825-1925, mainly published by Pigots 1825-6. Pay per view
- U.K. and U.S. Directories, 1680-1830
  www.ancestry.co.uk/search/db.aspx?dbid=3877
  Includes many Scottish directories. Pay per view

Ayrshire
- Ayrshire Roots: Directories
  www.ayrshireroots.com/Genealogy/Records/Directories/Directories.htm
  List of directories available, including copy of Pigot's *Ayrshire directory*, 1837

Berwickshire
See also Roxburghshire
- Berwickshire Directories
  www.genuki.org.uk/big/sct/BEW/directories.html
  Brief bibliography, with details of some reprints
- A Directory and Concise History of Berwick-upon-Tweed
  http://rgcairns.orpheusweb.co.uk/DirectoryContents.html
  Digitised images of an 1806 directory

Dumfriesshire
- Directories of Dumfries and Galloway: general directories of Scotland
  www.dgfhs.org.uk/Ian-Anderson/index.htm
  General discussion

Fife
- Directories held by Fife Council Libraries
  www.fifedirect.org.uk/uploadfiles/publications/c64_DirectoriesheldbyFifeCouncilLibraries.pdf
- Fife and Kinross Parochial Directory 1861
  www.dgnscrn.demon.co.uk/genuki/KRS/misc/parochial1861_1.html

- 1861 Parochial Directory
  www.fifefhs.org
  Click 'Records'. For Fife

Kinrossshire
See Fife

Kirkcudbrightshire
- List of residents of the Kirkcudbright area ... taken from the Stewartry directory of 1921-22
  www.old-kirkcudbright.net/genealogy/postal-g.asp

Lanarkshire
- First Glasgow Directory 1787
  www.ayrshireroots.com/Genealogy/Historical/Jones%20Directory.htm

Midlothian
- Edinburgh & Leith County Directories: Corstorphine
  www.angelfire.com/ct2/corstorphine/CorstorphineDirectories.html
  For various years 1842-1905
- Slaters Commercial Directory & topography of Scotland 1852: Corstorphine, Gogar & Neighbourhood
  www.angelfire.com/ct2/corstorphine/Slaters.html
- 1939-1940. Edinburgh Suburban Directory: Corstorphine
  www.angelfire.com/ct2/corstorphine/1940b.html
  Continued on 6 further pages

Peeblesshire
- Peeblesshire Directories
  www.genuki.org.uk/big/sct/PEE/directories.html
  Brief list

Roxburghshire
- Roxburghshire directories
  www.genuki.org.uk/big/sct/ROX/directories.html
  Brief list
- Rutherfurd's Southern Counties Register and Directory
  www.genuki.org.uk/big/sct/misc/ruth.html
  Brief description of an 1866 directory of Roxburghshire, Berwickshire and Selkirkshire, with notes on facsimile editions

Selkirkshire
See also Roxburghshire
- Selkirkshire Directories
  www.genuki.org.uk/big/sct/SEL/directories.html
  Brief list

Wigtownshire
- The Wigtown Directory 1912
  **http://homepages.rootsweb.ancestry.com/~scottish/
  TradeDirectory1912.html**

Educational Records
- National Archives of Scotland: Education Records
  www.nas.gov.uk/guides/education.asp
- Education
  www.scan.org.uk/knowledgebase/topics/education.htm
- Education Records
  **www.aberdeencity.gov.uk/nmsruntime/
  saveasdialog.asp?lID=16348&sID=1632**
  General introduction from Aberdeen City Archives
- Scottish School Records
  www.scan.org.uk/knowledgebase/topics/schoolrecords_topic.htm
- School Admission Registers
  www.scan.org.uk/knowledgebase/topics/schooladmissions.htm
- My Ancestor was a school pupil
  www.scan.org.uk/familyhistory/myancestor/schoolpupil.htm
- School Log Books
  www.scan.org.uk/knowledgebase/topics/schoollogbook.htm
- GASHE: Gateway to Archives of Scottish Higher Education
  www.gashe.ac.uk/about/index.html

Aberdeenshire
- Pitsligo School Log Book 1874-1912
  www.scan.org.uk/researchrtools/schoollogbook.htm

Ayrshire
- Marr College, Troon
  http://mypage.uniserve.ca/~imitchel/marrcoll.htm
  Register of pupils, 1935-2000

Roxburghshire

- Kelso Grammar School prizewinners of 1853
  www.genuki.org.uk:8080/big/sct/ROX/Kelso/1853schoolprizes.html

Stirlingshire

- Falkirk Council Cultural Services Guide to Archives: Education
  Records Finding Aid
  **www.falkirk.gov.uk/services/community/cultural_services/
  museums/archives/finding_aids/PDFs/education_records.pdf**

Electoral Rolls

Kirkcudbrightshire

- Parish of Urr Voters List - 1835
  http://donjaggi.net/galloway/urrvoters1835.html

Stirlingshire

- Falkirk Council Cultural Services Guide to Archives: Electoral Rolls and
  Valuation Rolls Finding Aid
  **www.falkirk.gov.uk/services/community/cultural_services/
  museums/archives/finding_aids/
  PDFs/valuation_and_electoral_roll.pdf**

Estate Records

See also Forfeited Estates Records, Sasines, & Trust Sederunt Books

- National Archives of Scotland: Estate Records
  www.nas.gov.uk/guides/estateRecords.asp
- National Archives of Scotland: Inheriting Land and Buildings
  www.nas.gov.uk/guides/inheriting.asp
- National Archives of Scotland: Private Papers
  www.nas.gov.uk/guides/privatePapers.asp
- Family Search Research Wiki: Scotland Land and Property
  https://wiki.familysearch.org/en/Scotland_Land_and_Property
- Family Search Research Wiki: Service of Heirs or Retours
  https://wiki.familysearch.org/en/Service_of_Heirs_or_Retours
- Property
  www.scan.org.uk/knowledgebase/topics/property_topic.htm
- My Ancestor was a Landowner
  www.scan.org.uk/familyhistory/myancestor/landowner.htm

- National Archives of Scotland: Buildings
  www.nas.gov.uk/guides/buildings.asp
  Sources for house history
- National Archives of Scotland: Deeds
  www.nas.gov.uk/guides/deeds.asp
- Land Registers and Valuation Rolls as Sources for Genealogy
  www.scotsgenealogy.com
  Click `on-line information' and title
- Virtual Vault: Property
  www.scan.org.uk/researchrtools/property.htm
- Scottish Land Records
  www.britishislesdna.com/Scotland/SCOT_land.htm
- Scotland Genealogy: Land Records - Deeds, Sasines, and
  Services of Heirs
  http://web.archive.org/web/20060502022626/
  http://www.gaia.edu/genclass/205/gen205_6.htm
  Introductory tutorial

Argyll

- The Argyll Estate
  http://keithdash.net/Argyllestate.html
- Black Book: List of Tenants on the Estate of Islay 1828
  **http://homepages.rootsweb.ancestry.com/~steve/islay/
  rawdata/blackbook/blackbook.htm**
- Rentals of Islay for the year from Whitsunday 1798 to Whitsun
  day 1799 Payable at Marts 1798 & Whits. 1799
  http://freepages.family.rootsweb.ancestry.com/~tlarson/tenantlist1799
- 1811 Tenants List
  **http://freepages.family.rootsweb.ancestry.com/~tlarson/
  tenantlist /islay1811tenantslist.htm**
  For Islay
- Kilchoman Islay Rentals 1733-1741
  **http://homepages.rootsweb.ancestry.com/~steve/islay/
  rawdata/rentals.htm**

Ayrshire

- Ayrshire Roots: Estate and Family Records
  **www.ayrshireroots.com/Genealogy/Records/
  Estate%20and%20Family/Estate%20and%20Family.htm**

East Lothian
- Land and Property Records in East Lothian
  www.clerkington.plus.com/GENUKI/ELN/landAndProperty.html

Fife
- Sheriff Court of Fife Deeds, 1715-1809
  www.fifefhs.org
  Click on `Records' and title. This website also has collections of deeds for Auchtermuchty, Burntisland, Crail, Culross, Cupar, Dunfermline, Dysart, Inverkeithing, Kinghorn, Kirkcaldy, Pittenweem, and St. Andrews

Orkney
- Land and Ownership
  www.genuki.org.uk/big/sct/OKI/land.html
  Discussion of landownership in Orkney

Exchequer Records
- National Archives of Scotland: Exchequer Records
  www.nas.gov.uk/guides/exchequer.asp

Farm Horse Tax Records
- Scotland's Places: Farm Horse Tax 1797-1798.
  www.scotlandsplaces.gov.uk/digital_vols/
  all_vols.php?vol_id=1&return=county

Ayrshire
- [Buittle Horse Tax 1797]
  www.buittle.org.uk/neworder/horsetax.htm
- Parish of Urr Horse Tax - 1797
  http://donjaggi.net/galloway/urrhorsetax.html

Forfeited Estates Records
- Declared Accounts: Forfeited Estates
  www.british-history.ac.uk/report.aspx?compid=85507
- Genealogical Index to *Statistics of the Annexed Estates, 1755-1756, from the records of the Forfeited Estates preserved in the Scottish Record Office* [now National Archives of Scotland]; Edinburgh, HMSO, 1973.
  www.kinhelp.co.uk/KinHelp/genealogical-indices/gene11

Friendly Society Records
- Friendly Societies and Similar Bodies
  www.scan.org.uk/knowledgebase/topics/friendlysocieties_topic.htm

Justice of the Peace Records
- National Archives of Scotland: Justice of the Peace Records
  www.nas.gov.uk/guides/justice.asp

Kirk Sessions Records
See Church Records

Land Ownership Records
See also Estate Records
- Scotland's Places: Land Ownership Commission 1872-3
  www.scotlandsplaces.gov.uk/digital_vols/all_vols.php?vol_id=3
  Lists everyone who owned more than 1 acre of land

Wigtownshire
- M'Kerlie's Wigtownshire Estates, Properties and Farms
  http://freepages.history.rootsweb.ancestry.com/~leighann/
  mkerlie/mkerlie.html

Lieutenancy Records
- Lieutenancy Book, County of Roxburgh 1797-1802
  www.scan.org.uk/researchrtools/lieutenancy.htm
  Includes lists of men balloted in each parish to serve in the militia

Medical Records
- Hospital Records Database
  www.nationalarchives.gov.uk/hospitalrecords

Lanarkshire
- NHS Greater Glasgow and Clyde Archives
  www.archives.gla.ac.uk/gghb/default.html

Midlothian
- Lothian Health Services Archives
  www.lhsa.lib.ed.ac.uk
  For patient and staff records, *etc.*

Stirlingshire

- Information on Medical Records for Family Historians
  www.falkirk.gov.uk/services/community/cultural_services/
  museums/archives/medical_records_for_familiy_history.pdf
  In the Falkirk area

Municipal and Parochial Records

- National Archives of Scotland: Burgh Records
  www.nas.gov.uk/guides/burgh.asp
- Scottish Burghs
  www.scan.org.uk/knowledgebase/topics/burgh.htm

Aberdeenshire

- Genealogical index to *Extracts from the records of the Aberdeen Burgh 1625-1642*. Published: Scottish Burgh Records Society, 1871
  www.kinhelp.co.uk/KinHelp/genealogical-indices/gene4

Angus

- Genealogical Index to *Charters, Writs, and public documents of the Royal Burgh of Dundee 1292-1880*. Published Dundee 1880
  www.kinhelp.co.uk/KinHelp/genealogical-indices/gene9

Ayrshire

- Maybole Archives
  www.maybole.org/history/Archives
  Includes list of burgesses, 15th October 1834, Maybole councillors, 1722-1828, the stent rolls of Maybole 1816-1832, *etc.*

Dumfriesshire

- Chamberlain's Accounts 1793-1801
  www.dgcommunity.net/historicalindexes/chamberlains.aspx
  For Dumfries
- Notices from the local records of Dysart
  www.scotsfind.org/dysart_access/dysart.pdf
  Originally published 1853

Fife

- Index to *Extracts from the Burgh records of Dunfermline in 16th and 17th centuries;* Published: Carnegie Dunfermline Trust, 1951.
  www.kinhelp.co.uk/KinHelp/genealogical-indices/gene7

Kirkcudbrightshire

- Kirkcudbright Burgh Stent Rolls
  www.old-kirkcudbright.net/genealogy/stent/index.asp
  For 1779, 1790 and 1806

Lanarkshire

- Glasgow, Records of the Burgh: Extracts from the Burgh records, 1573-1690
  www.british-history.ac.uk/place.aspx?gid=88&region=7
  Digitised from printed volumes
- Glasgow Charters: Transcripts of Charters and Documents, 1175-1649
  www.british-history.ac.uk/place.aspx?gid=93&region=7
  Digitised from printed volumes
- A genealogical index to *Extracts from the records of the Burgh of Glasgow, volume 1 (Minutes & accounts, 1573-1642)*
  www.kinhelp.co.uk/KinHelp/genealogical-indices/gene1
  Continued for 1630-62 at **/gene2**

Midlothian

- Edinburgh, Records of the Burgh
  www.british-history.ac.uk/place.aspx?gid=110&region=7
  Printed extracts, 1403-1589

Peeblesshire

- Genealogical Index to *Charters and documents relating to the Burgh of Peebles, with extracts from the records of the burgh A.D.1165-1710..* [note: burgh minutes begin in the year 1456]
  www.kinhelp.co.uk/KinHelp/genealogical-indices/gene8

Selkirkshire

- Index to *The Burgh Court book of Selkirk, Part One: 1503-1531*; (published by the Scottish Record Society, 1960).
  www.kinhelp.co.uk/KinHelp/genealogical-indices/gene12
  Continued for 1531-41 at **/gene13**

Stirlingshire

- Town Council Minutes of the Royal Burgh of Stirling 1847-1864 Stirling Council Archives (SB1/1/1)
  www.scan.org.uk/researchrtools/stirling_minutes.htm

Newspapers

- Family Search Research Wiki: Scotland Newspapers
  https://wiki.familysearch.org/en/Scotland_Newspapers
- National Library of Scotland: Rare Books Collections: Newspapers
  www.nls.uk/collections/rarebooks/collections/newspapers.html
- Online Newspapers.com: Scotland
  www.onlinenewspapers.com/scotland.htm
  Links to Scottish newspaper sites
- Newsplan Scotland
  www.nls.uk/professional/newsplanscotland
  Project to microfilm newspapers; includes list of titles
- Historical Newspaper Collection
  www.ancestry.co.uk/search/rectype/periodicals/news/default.aspx
  Includes *Edinburgh Advertiser,* 1771-1909, *Edinburgh Courant,* 1884-1884, *Edinburgh Weekly Journal,* 1801-1808, Perth, Scotland Newspaper Index Cards, 1809-1990, *Scotsman,* 1945-1945, *The Edinburgh Chronicle,* 1759-1760, and The *Edinburgh Evening Courant,* 1867-1869
- British Newspapers 1800-1900
  http://newspapers.bl.uk/blcs
  Includes a number of digitised Scottish newspapers
- British Library Newspaper Collections
  www.bl.uk/reshelp/findhelprestype/news/blnewscoll
  The collection includes many Scottish newspapers
- The Scotsman Digital Archive
  http://archive.scotsman.com
  Digitised images of all issues, 1817-1950, fully indexed
- Viv Dunstan's indexes: pre-1855 Scotsman death notices
  www.vivdunstan.co.uk/indexes/scotsman1855.html

Angus

- Angus Council: Newspapers for Researchers
  www.angus.gov.uk/history/features/2003-06-newspapers.htm

Ayrshire

- Ayrshire Roots: Newspapers
  www.ayrshireroots.com/Genealogy/Records/Newspapers/
  Newspapers.htm

- Ayrshire Ancestors Namesearch
  www.ayrshireancestors.co.uk/NameSearch.htm
  Includes index to births marriages & deaths in the *Ayr Advertiser* for selected years from 1834

Berwickshire

- Berwickshire newspapers
  www.genuki.org.uk/big/sct/BEW/newspaperList.html
- Viv Dunstan's indexes: pre-1855 *Kelso Chronicle* death notices
  www.vivdunstan.co.uk/indexes/kelso1855.html

Fife

- A List of Historical Newspapers held in Fife Council Libraries
  www.fifedirect.org.uk/publications/index.cfm?fuseaction=
  publication.pop&pubid=D396FA5E-B5AD-5EE2-
  A8D44A50F1FEB74F
- Fife, Scotland, Cupar Library Newspaper Index Cards, 1833-1987
  http://search.ancestry.co.uk/iexec/?htx=List&dbid=
  1206&offerid=0%3a7858%3a0
  Pay per view

Perthshire

- Perth, Scotland Newspaper Index Cards, 1809-1990
  http://search.ancestry.co.uk/iexec/?htx=List&dbid=
  1220&offerid=0%3a7858%3a0
  Pay per view

Renfrewshire

- Watt Library newspaper index
  www.inverclyde.gov.uk/GeneralR.aspx?id=829&catid=1792
  Covers Greenock area
- Watt Library Newsplan
  www.inverclyde.gov.uk/GeneralR3a.aspx?id=710&catid=1792

Roxburghshire

- Roxburghshire Newspapers
  www.genuki.org.uk/big/sct/ROX/newspaperList.html
  List of old newspapers

Selkirkshire

- Selkirkshire Newspapers
  www.genuki.org.uk/big/sct/SEL/newspaperList.html
  List

Nonconformist Records

See also Salvation Army Records, and chapter 8 for birth, marriage, and death registers

- Protestant Nonconformity in Scotland: an introduction
  www.genuki.org.uk/big/sct/noncon1.html
  Continued at **/noncon2.html**

Angus

- Family Search Research Wiki: Dundee Nonconformist Church Records
  **https://wiki.familysearch.org/en/Dundee_Nonconformist_
                                       Church_Records**

Fife

- Family Search Research Wiki: Kirkcaldy Nonconformist Church Records
  **https://wiki.familysearch.org/en/Kirkcaldy_
                              Nonconformist_Church_Records**

Lanarkshire

- Family Search Research Wiki: Glasgow Nonconformist Church Records
  **https://wiki.familysearch.org/en/Glasgow_
                              Nonconformist_Church_Records**

Midlothian

- Family Search Research Wiki: Edinburgh Nonconformist Church Records
  **https://wiki.familysearch.org/en/Edinburgh_
                              Nonconformist_Church_Records**

Parliamentary Papers

- Parliamentary Papers
  **www.scan.org.uk/knowledgebase/topics/
                      parliamentarypapers_topic.htm**

Parliamentary Records

- National Archives of Scotland: Scottish Parliament Records
  www.nas.gov.uk/guides/scottishParliament.asp

Passenger Lists

- Passenger Lists
  www.scan.org.uk/knowledgebase/topics/topicpassengerlists.htm
- My Ancestor was a Passenger on a Ship
  www.scan.org.uk/familyhistory/myancestor/shippassenger.htm
- Ships from Scotland to America, 1628-1828
  **http://search.ancestry.co.uk/iexec/?htx=BookList&dbid=
                              49363&offerid=0%3a7858%3a**
  Originally published Genealogical Publishing Co., 2002. Pay per view
- Passenger Lists of Ships leaving Scotland
  www.scotlandsfamily.com/ships-passengers.htm
  Gateway to passenger list sites
- Ship Passenger Lists: Scot & Irish
  www.ralstongenealogy.com/sislist.htm

Passports

- Passports
  www.scan.org.uk/researchrtools/passports.htm
- My Ancestor was a passport holder
  www.scan.org.uk/familyhistory/myancestor/passport.htm

Photographs

- Scotland in Photographs
  www.scan.org.uk/knowledgebase/topics/photocollections.htm

Poor Law

- Caring for the poor, sick and needy: A brief history of poor relief in Scotland
  **www.aberdeencity.gov.uk/nmsruntime/
                              saveasdialog.asp?lID=16350&sID=163**
  From Aberdeen City Archives
- National Archives of Scotland: Records of the Poor
  www.nas.gov.uk/guides/poor.asp

- My Ancestor was a Pauper
  www.scan.org.uk/familyhistory/myancestor/pauper.htm
- Poor Relief
  www.scan.org.uk/knowledgebase/topics/poorrelief.htm
- Virtual Vault: Poor Relief Records
  www.scan.org.uk/researchrtools/poorrelief.htm
  Digitised examples of typical records
- The Workhouse
  users.ox.ac.uk/~peter/workhouse
  Includes lists of Scottish `poorhouses' and almshouses, with many transcripts of 1881 census returns (not listed in chapter 10)

Angus
- Poorhouses
  www.fdca.org.uk/FDCAPoorHouses.html
  In Dundee
- Friends of Dundee City Archives: Index of Poor Registers
  www.fdca.org.uk/FDCAPoorIndexes.html
  For Dundee, 1854-78

Ayrshire
- Ayrshire Poor Relief Database
  www.ayrshire-roots.co.uk/poorrelief.php
- Ayrshire Roots: Poor Relief Records
  www.ayrshireroots.com/Genealogy/Records/
  Poor%20Relief/Poor%20Relief.htm
  Includes transcripts from Kilwinning and Stevenston, with list of records at Ayrshire Archives, *etc.*
- Dreghorn Poor Relief: Register of Applications for Poor Relief in the parish of Dreghorn, Ayrshire
  www.troonayrshirefhs.org.uk/dreghorn.html
  Transcript, 1872-90

  Kilbirnie Parish Council Record of Applications, 1859-1862
  www.ayrshirearchives.org.uk/pdfs/
  Kilbirnie-poor-relief-1859-1862-CO3-41-25.pdf

- Maybole Morsels
  www.maybole.org/history/Archives/morsels/ListofPoor.htm
  includes poor lists of 1905, 1907, 1911, & 1915
- Poor Relief at Stevenston Parish
  www.threetowners.com/Stevenston/poor_relief_stevenston.htm

Dumfriesshire
- Dumfries Poor Board Minutes
  www.dgcommunity.net/historicalindexes/poorboard.aspx
  For 1855-95

Fife
- Cupar Sheriff Court Aliment Decrees 1830-1854
  www.fifefhs.org/Records/cupardecrees.htm
- Aliment Decrees, Dunfermline Sheriff Court, 1830-1854
  www.fifefhs.org/Records/dunfaliments.htm
- Saline Paupers 1845-1852
  www.fifefhs.org
  Click on `records' and title

Kirkcudbrightshire
- Kirkcudbright Parochial Board Appeals, 1848
  www.old-kirkcudbright.net/genealogy/appeals.asp
  Appeals against Poor Rate valuations

Roxburghshire
- Borders Family History Society: Poor Law Records Search
  www.bordersfhs.org.uk/BFHSPoorLawsearchform.asp
  Currently only indexes records for Jedburgh 1852-93

Portraits
- Angus People Image Index
  www.angus.gov.uk/history/archives/resources/
  peopleimageindex/default.htm
  Index to people portrayed in books in Angus archives and libraries

Probate Records
See Wills

Quaker Records

- Quaker Family History Society: Scotland
  www.rootsweb.ancestry.com/~engqfhs/Research/counties/scots.htm
  Notes on Quaker records
- Scottish Quakers and Early America, 1650-1700 / David Dobson
  http://search.ancestry.co.uk/iexec/?htx=BookList&dbid=
  48516&offerid=0%3a7858%3a0
  Originally published Genealogical Publishing Co., 1998. Pay per view

Registrars & Registration Districts

- General Register Office Scotland: List of Parishes and Registration Districts
  www.gro-scotland.gov.uk/famrec/list-of-parishes-
  registration-districts.html

Ayrshire

- Registrars of Births, Deaths and Marriages in Ayrshire
  www.ayrshireroots.com/Genealogy/Records/Registrars/
  Registrars.htm
- Registration Offices in Ayrshire
  www.rootsweb.com/~sctayr/regaddre.html

Fife

- Registration Offices
  www.genuki.org.uk/big/sct/FIF/Registrars.htm
  In Fife
- Fife Registration Districts Names and Numbers
  www.thefifepost.com/FifeRegDist.htm

Orkney

- Orkney Islands Council: Registrars
  www.orkney.gov.uk/nqcontent.cfm?a_id=9492&tt=orkneyv2

Perthshire

- Perth & Kinross Family History Centre
  www.pkc.gov.uk/Law+and+licensing/Birth+marriage+civil+
  partnership+and+death/Family+History+Centre

Ross & Cromarty

- Registration Service Ancestry Research: Genealogy and Family Searches at Stornoway Registration Office
  www.w-isles.gov.uk/registrars/ancestry.asp

Roman Catholic Records

- Scottish Catholic Heritage: Network of Archives and Libraries of the Catholic Church: Scottish Catholic Archives
  www.catholic-heritage.net
  Click 'Partner Institutions'

Kirkcudbrightshire

- Roman Catholics in Buittle
  http://buittle.org.uk/neworder/munches/1704-list.htm

Salvation Army Records

- Salvation Army International Heritage Centre
  www1.salvationarmy.org/heritage.nsf

Sasines

- National Archives of Scotland: The Register of Sasines
  www.nas.gov.uk/guides/sasines.asp
- Sasine Abridgements
  www.scan.org.uk/knowledgebase/topics/sasine_abbs_topic.htm
- Family Search Research Wiki: Sasines
  https://wiki.familysearch.org/en/Sasines

Sheriff Court Records

- National Archives of Scotland: Sheriff Court Records
  www.nas.gov.uk/guides/sheriffCourt.asp

Angus

- Index to Records of Dundee Sheriff Court
  www.genuki.org.uk/big/sct/ANS/Topics/sc45.html
- Index to Records of Forfar Sheriff Court
  www.genuki.org.uk:8080/big/sct/ANS/Topics/sc47.html

Fife

- Aberdour Jurors 1851
  www.fifefhs.org/Records/Jurors/aberdourjurors.htm
- Auchtertool Jurors 1851
  www.fifefhs.org/Records/Jurors/auchtertooljurors.htm
- Ballingry Jurors 1851
  www.fifefhs.org/Records/Jurors/ballingryjurors.htm
- Carnock Jurors 1851
  www.fifefhs.org/Records/Jurors/carnockjurors.htm
- Dalgety Jurors 1851
  www.fifefhs.org/Records/Jurors/dalgetyjurors.htm
- Saline Jurors 1851
  www.fifefhs.org/Records/Jurors/salinejurors.htm
- Torryburn Jurors 1851
  www.fifefhs.org/Records/Jurors/torryburnjurors.htm

State Papers

- National Archives of Scotland: State papers
  www.nas.gov.uk/guides/statePapers.asp
- State Papers, Scotland; Calendar
  www.british-history.ac.uk/place.aspx?gid=85&region=7
  Digitised from printed volumes
  National Library of Scotland: Family History: State Papers of Scotland
  www.nls.uk/family-history/state-papers/index.html

Statistical Accounts

- The Statistical Accounts of Scotland 1791-1845
  http://edina.ac.uk/stat-acc-scot/description.html

Tax Records

See also Farm Horse Tax Records
- National Archives of Scotland: Taxation Records
  www.nas.gov.uk/guides/taxation.asp
- Virtual Vault: Tax Records
  www.scan.org.uk/researchrtools/tax.htm
  Digitised examples of typical records
  Family Search Research Wiki: Scotland Taxation
  https://wiki.familysearch.org/en/Scotland_Taxation

- Scottish Genealogy Society Information Leaflet: Scottish Poll Tax
  www.scotsgenealogy.com
  Click `on-line information' & title

Aberdeenshire

- Glenbuchat in the Poll Book of 1696
  http://members.shaw.ca/doughay/poll1696.htm
  Poll tax

Angus

- Taxation Records
  www.genuki.org.uk/big/sct/ANS/Topics/tax.html
  List of tax assessments for Angus
- Extract from the 1691 Hearth Tax Records for the Parishes of Monikie and Lundie, Scotland
  www.monikie.org.uk/ah-hearthtax.htm

Ayrshire

- The Hearth Tax for Ayrshire, 1691
  www.maybole.org/history/archives/hearthtax1691.htm
  Assessment for Maybole

Kirkcudbrightshire

- Window Tax Records
  www.buittle.org.uk/neworder/windowtax.htm
  For Buittle, 1748-95

Lanarkshire

- Cess Book for the County of Lanarkshire 1724-1725
  www.scan.org.uk/researchrtools/cess.htm
  The cess was a tax on land; this book lists taxpayers, i.e. landowners

Sutherland

- Golspie People 1798
  www.countysutherland.co.uk/57.html
  List of taxpayers

Trust Sederunt Books

- Trust Sederunt Books
  www.scan.org.uk/knowledgebase/topics/trustsederuntbooks.htm
  These relate to family trusts arising from wills, marriage settlements, or personal incapacity

Valuation Rolls

See also Electoral Rolls & Estate Records

- Valuation Rolls
  www.scan.org.uk/knowledgebase/topics/valrolls_topic.htm
- National Archives of Scotland: Valuation Rolls
  www.nas.gov.uk/guides/valuationRolls.asp
- My Ancestor was a Ratepayer
  www.scan.org.uk/familyhistory/myancestor/ratepayer.htm

Angus

- Monikie, Scotland: Valuation Roll 1904-05
  www.monikie.org.uk/ah-monikievalroll.htm

Ayrshire

- Ayrshire Roots: Valuation Rolls
  www.ayrshireroots.com/Genealogy/Records/Valuation%20Rolls/Valuation%20Rolls.htm

Dumfriesshire

- Graham Maxwell Ancestry: Free Resources: Dumfriesshire Valuation Roll (1896-97)
  www.maxwellancestry.com/ancestry/resources/dumfriesshirevaluationroll.htm

Fife

- Valuation Rolls held by Fife Council Libraries
  www.fifedirect.org.uk/publications/index.cfm?fuseaction=publication.pop&pubid=D38A5B1A-D154-41A6-D63DE5A19E0C
- Valuation Roll - Forgan Parish - 1855
  www.twentytwoglassroad.co.uk/Newport/1855VR.htm
  Further pages cover 1860 /**1860VR.htm** and 1871 /**1871vr.htm**

Kirkcudbrightshire

- Valuation Rolls, Buittle Parish
  http://buittle.org.uk/valuaton.htm
  Transcripts of 8 rolls, 18-20th c.
- Old Kirkcudbright: Some Records of Lands and their Owners In Galloway
  www.old-kirkcudbright.net/landowners/index.asp
  Reproduces several valuations, late-18th c. - 1859/60

Lanarkshire

- The Glasgow Story: Valuation Rolls 1913-1914
  www.theglasgowstory.com/valindex.php

Vehicle Registration Licences

- Vehicle Registration
  www.scan.org.uk/knowledgebase/topics/vehicleregistration.htm

Perthshire

- Friends of Dundee Archives: Vehicle Registrations
  www.fdca.org.uk/FDCAVehicleRegs.html
  Database for Perthshire, 1909-11, & Kinross, 1904-52

War Memorials, Rolls of Honour *etc.*

- Commonwealth War Graves Commission Debt of Honour Register
  www.cwgc.org
- Scottish National War Memorial
  www.snwm.org
  Official site; includes database of the Scottish Roll of Honour
- Roll of Honour
  www.roll-of-honour.com
  Includes War memorials for parishes in all Scottish counties
- The Scottish War Graves Project
  http://scottishwargraves.phpbbweb.com
- War Memorials across Scotland
  http://web.archive.org/web/20070901230500/www.moirbooks.homestead.com/warmemorials.html

Aberdeenshire

- Corgarff and Strathdon War Memorials
  http://users.tinyonline.co.uk/amchardy/WarMemorials/Frontpage.htm

- The Fallen
  www.kinnethmont.co.uk/war-memorials.htm
  War Memorials of Kennethmont, Gartly, Rhynie & Kearn, Clatt,
  Huntly & Drumblade, Aberdeenshire`
- Lumsden War Memorial
  http://users.tinyonline.co.uk/amchardy/Lumsden/Lumsden.htm
- Towie War Memorial
  http://users.tinyonline.co.uk/amchardy/Towie/Towie.htm

Angus
- 5th (Angus & Dundee) Battalion: The Black Watch
  www.royalhighlanders.co.uk
  Includes war memorials and roll of honour 1914-21 pages
- Dundee War Records
  www.fdca.org.uk/FDCAWarRecords.html
  Includes Dundee war memorials, and Dundee roll of honour, 1914-19
- City of Dundee Roll of Honour World War II 1939 to 1945
  www.dundeecity.gov.uk/roh

Argyll
- Campbeltown War Memorial
  http://freepages.genealogy.rootsweb.ancestry.com/~djmack/index.html
- War Memorials within the Parish of Glenorchy and Innishail Argyll
  www.loch-awe.com/community/warmemorial2.htm
- [Inveraray War Memorial]
  http://web.archive.org/web/20041214145603/
  http://argyllroots.co.uk/inveraray_list.htm

  Kintyre, Scotland, War Memorials
  www.ralstongenealogy.com/warmemorialquery.php
  Includes memorials from Auchencorvie, Barr, Campbeltown, Carradale,
  Clachan and Southend

Ayrshire
- Ayrshire World War Casualty Database
  www.ayrshire-roots.co.uk/casualty.php
- Ardrossan WWI Roll of Honour
  www.threetowners.com/Ard%20folder/ardr_ww1.htm

- Dalry WWI Roll of Honour
  www.threetowners.com/Dalry/ww1_memorial.htm
- Kilwinning WWI Roll of Honour
  www.threetowners.com/Kilwinning/ww1_roll_of_honour.htm
- Memorials
  www.maybole.org/history/Archives/Memorials/memorials.htm
  War memorials of Maybole
- Saltcoats WW1 Roll of Honour
  www.threetowners.com/Saltcoats/saltcoats_ww1.htm
- Stevenston WWI Roll of Honour
  www.threetowners.com/Stevenston/roll_of_honour_ww1.htm
- West Kilbride WWI Roll of Honour
  www.threetowners.com/West%20Kilbride/ww1_memorial.htm

Berwickshire
- Lauder War Memorial
  www.lauder.bordernet.co.uk/history/articles/war-memorials.html

Caithness
- Highland Archives: Caithness Roll of Honour 1914-1919 (Army)
  www.internet-promotions.co.uk/archives/caithness/roll/
- Caithness War Memorials
  www.caithness.org/atoz/warmemorials/index.htm

Dunbartonshire
- West Dunbartonshire Council: War Memorials
  www.west-dunbarton.gov.uk/community-and-living/war-memorials/
- List of Fatal Casualties ... Burgh of Clydebank, Glasgow, Scotland
  http://thor.prohosting.com/~hughw/wardead1.txt
  Continued in **/wardead2.txt** (up to **6**)

Lanarkshire
- The University of Glasgow Story: First World War Roll of Honour
  www.universitystory.gla.ac.uk/ww1-intro
- *Evening Times* Roll of Honour
  www.glasgow.gov.uk/en/Residents/Library_Services/
  Family_Local_History/eveningtimesrollofhonour.htm
  1st World War roll for Glasgow

- War Memorials within South Lanarkshire
  www.southlanarkshire.gov.uk/portal/page/portal/
  SLC_PUBLICDOCUMENTS/Comm/
  COMM_654_War_Memorials.pdf
- Remembered with Honour: Forth, Lanarkshire, War Memorial
  www.forth.themutual.net/warmemorials.html

Midlothian
- Corstorphine War Dead Great War Memorial 1914-1918
  www.angelfire.com/ct2/corstorphine/index8.html
- Corstorphine War Dead 1939-1945
  www.angelfire.com/ct2/corstorphine/index8a.html
- St. Giles Cathedral, Edinburgh
  www.btinternet.com/%7ejames.fanning/edinburgh/index.html
  World War I memorials

Nairnshire
- Cawdor War Memorial Cairn
  http://www.spanglefish.com/CWMC/index.asp?pageid=41469

Orkney
- Orkney War Memorials
  www.rbls-kirkwall.org.uk/memorials.html

Renfrewshire
- Lochwinnoch War Memorial, Renfrewshire.
  www.happyhaggis.co.uk/renfrew-lochwinnoch.htm

Roxburghshire
- Maxton War Memorial
  www.maxton.bordernet.co.uk/war-memorial.html
- Ednam War Memorial
  www.ednam.bordernet.co.uk/history/memorial.html

Selkirkshire
- Innerleithen War Memorial 1914-1918
  www.scotlandgenweb.org/selkirkshire/innerleithmemorial.html

Stirlingshire
- Kilsyth War Memorial
  www.paperclip.org.uk/kilsythweb/history/archivesources/
  kilsyth_war_memorial.htm

Sutherland
- A Tribute to the Men of Sutherland who Gave their Lives in Two
  World Wars
  http://cosuthtribute.blogspot.com/
  Includes many pages for particular places

West Lothian
- War Memorials / Rolls of Honour
  www.wlfhs.org.uk
  Click title on side-bar
- Korean War Memorial
  www.wlfhs.org.uk
  Click title on side-bar
- Uphall on the Web: War Memorial
  www.uphall.org/index.php?option=com_content&view=
  article&id=129&Itemid=14
  See also **=140**

Wigtownshire
- Lest We Forget
  http://freepages.history.rootsweb.ancestry.com/~leighann/
  memorials/war.htm
  Wigtownshire war memorials

Wills
See also Trust Sederunt Books
- Family Search Research Wiki: Scotland Probate Records
  https://wiki.familysearch.org/en/Scotland_Probate_Records
- Scotlands People: Wills and Testaments
  http://scotlandspeople.gov.uk/content/help/index.aspx?r=554&407
  Pay per view site. Images and index. Important database
- National Archives of Scotland: Wills and Testaments
  www.nas.gov.uk/guides/wills.asp

- Scottish Probate Records
  http://www.britishislesdna.com/Scotland/SCOT_probate.htm
- Probate in Scotland 1500 to 1901 / Sherry Irvine
  www.ancestry.com/learn/library/article.aspx?article=7286
  General introduction
- Wills and Testaments
  www.scan.org.uk/knowledgebase/topics/
  **   willsandtestaments_topic.htm**
- National Archives of Scotland: Soldiers' and Airmen's Wills 1857-1964
  www.nas.gov.uk/guides/soldiersWills.asp
- Scottish Jamaica Testaments
  www.scotsgenealogy.com
  Click 'on-line information' and title

Aberdeenshire

- Aberdeen, Scotland, Register of testaments 1715-1800
  www.ancestry.com/search/db.aspx?dbid=6344
  Pay per view database

Argyll

- Commissariot Record of The Isles: Register of Testaments, 1661-1800 /
  Francis J. Grant (ed)
  http://freepages.folklore.rootsweb.ancestry.com/~tlarson/
  **   islaywillrecords.htm**
  Originally published by the Scottish Record Society, 1902

Ayrshire

- Ayrshire Roots: testaments, wills, and other source documents
  www.ayrshireroots.com/Genealogy/Records/Wills/WILLs.htm
  Of general Scottish interest, as well as Ayrshire

Invernessshire

- The Commissariat Record of Inverness: Register of Testaments
  1630-1800
  scotsfind.org/inverness_access/inverness.pdf
  Originally published by the Index Society, 1897

Lanarkshire

- The Commissariat Record of Hamilton and Campsie: Register
  of Testaments 1564-1800
  www.scotsfind.org/databases_free/hamilton.pdf
  Originally published British Record Society Scottish Section, 1898
- The Commissariot Record of Hamilton and Campsie
  http://search.ancestry.co.uk/iexec/?htx=BookList&dbid=
  **   28546&offerid=0%3a7858%3a0**
  As above. Originally published British Record Society Scottish
  Section, 1898. Pay per view

Midlothian

- The Commissariat Record of Edinburgh: Register of Testaments
  Part 1. Volume 1 to 35. 1514-1600
  www.scotsfind.org/databases_free/edinburgh.pdf
  Originally published British Record Society, 1897
- The Commissariot Record of Edinburgh, Register of Testaments.
  http://search.ancestry.co.uk/iexec/?htx=BookList&dbid=
  **   28542&offerid=0%3a7858%3a0**
  Originally published British Record Society, 1897. Pay per view
- 16th century testaments of people with Inveresk connexions,
  1514-1600
  www.ancestor.abel.co.uk/inv/test16.html
  Further pages covers 17th c. **/test17.html** & 18th c. **/test18.html**

Wigtownshire

- The Commissariat Record of Wigtown Testaments 1700-1800 /
  Francis J. Grant (ed.)
  http://freepages.history.rootsweb.ancestry.com/~leighann/
  **   wills/in tro2.html**

12. Occupational Records

If you know the occupations of your ancestors, you potentially have the key to open up a wide range of sources. Occupational records frequently provide invaluable details of the lives and careers of our forebears. Useful online lists of historic occupations include:

- National Archives of Scotland: Crafts and Trades
  www.nas.gov.uk/guides/crafts.asp
- Family Search Research Wiki: Scotland Occupations
  https://wiki.familysearch.org/en/Scotland_Occupations
- Old Names of Occupations
  www.scottap.com/family/Lanark/occupations.html
- Old Occupations in Scotland: What exactly did you say your ancestor did?
  www.scotroots.com/occupations.htm
  Dictionary

Airmen
- Looking for Records of an Airman in the Royal Air Force
  **www.nationalarchives.gov.uk/gettingstarted/
  looking-for-person/airmanraf.htm**

Apprentices
- The Register of Apprentices of the City of Edinburgh
  www.scotsfind.org/databases_free/apprentice.pdf
  Covers 1583-1800. Digitised images of Record Society publications
- Boys from Inveresk who were apprenticed to burgesses of Edinburgh, 1583-1800
  www.ancestor.abel.co.uk/inv/app.html
- Boys from Liberton who were apprenticed to burgesses of Edinburgh, 1583-1800
  www.ancestor.abel.co.uk/lib/app.html

Architects
- Dictionary of Scottish Architects 1840-1980
  www.scottisharchitects.org.uk

Artists
- Scottish Genealogy Society Information Leaflet: Artists
  www.scotsgenealogy.com
  Click on 'on-line information' and title
- Glasgow School of Art Archives
  www.gsa.ac.uk/gsa.cfm?pid=2206

Bankers and Bank Customers
- Royal Bank of Scotland: Our Archives
  www.rbs.com
  Click on 'About us', 'Our Heritage', and 'Our Archives'

Book Trades
- Scottish Book Trade Index
  www.nls.uk/catalogues/resources/sbti/index.html
  Index of printers, publishers, bookbinders, *etc.,* to 1850

Brewers
- Scottish Brewing Archive
  www.archives.gla.ac.uk/sba/default.html

Brickmaking
- My Ancestor ... worked in the Brickmaking Industries
  **www.falkirk.gov.uk/services/community/cultural_services/
  museums/archives/brickmaking.pd**
  In the Falkirk area

Burgesses
- My Ancestor was a Burgess
  www.scan.org.uk/familyhistory/myancestor/burgess.htm
- Roll of Edinburgh Burgesses and Guild-Brethren, 1406-1841
  www.scotsfind.org/burgesses_access/burgesses.pdf
  www.scotsfind.org/databases_free/burgesses.pdf
  Digitised images of a Scottish Record Society publication

Canal Workers
- National Archives of Scotland: Canal Records
  www.nas.gov.uk/guides/canal.asp

- My Ancestor ... Worked on the Canals
  **www.falkirk.gov.uk/services/community/cultural_services/
  museums/archives/canals.pdf**
  In the Falkirk area

Clergy
- Your ancestor was a Scottish clergyman: Published Sources for
  Scottish clergymen described and assessed
  **www.kinhelp.co.uk/KinHelp/genealogical-resources-hints/
  your-ancestor-was-a-scottish-clergyman/
  ?searchterm=glasgow**
- Scottish Ministers and their Families
  www.dwalker.pwp.blueyonder.co.uk/fastinew.htm
  Details of a CD
- Fasti Ecclesiæ Scoticanæ: the succession of ministers in the Church of
  Scotland from the reformation / Hew Scott
  http://openlibrary.org/b/OL7039322M/Fasti_ecclesiæ_scoticanæ
  Originally published 1916

Criminals, Convicts & Prisoners
- National Archives of Scotland: How to Search for High Court
  Criminal Trials
  www.nas.gov.uk/guides/highCourt.asp
- National Archives of Scotland: Crime and Criminals
  www.nas.gov.uk/guides/crime.asp
- My Ancestor was a Prisoner
  www.scan.org.uk/familyhistory/myancestor/prisoner.htm
- Prisons and Prisoners
  www.scan.org.uk/knowledgebase/topics/prisons_topic.htm
- Scottish Criminal Justice
  **www.ayrshireroots.com/Genealogy/Reference/
  Scottish%20Criminal%20Justice.htm**
  Including details of records

Argyll
- Inveraray Jail: Prison Records
  www.inverarayjail.co.uk/prison-records/index.asp

Dumfriesshire
- Jail and Bail Bond Books at Dumfries
  www.dgcommunity.net/historicalindexes/jail.aspx
  Index of prisoners, 1714-88 for Dumfriesshire and Kirkcudbrightshire

Kincardineshire
- The Black Book of Kincardineshire
  http://myweb.tiscali.co.uk/nescotland/articles/blkbk.htm
  Details of 17th c. criminals

Kirkcudbrightshire
See Dumfriesshire

Firemen
Stirlingshire
- Falkirk Council Gultural Services Guide to Archives: Fire &
  Rescue Services Finding Aid
  **www.falkirk.gov.uk/services/community/cultural_services/
  museums/archives/finding_aids/PDFs/
  central_scotland_fire_rescue.pdf**

Gypsies
- The Scottish Gypsies
  www.scottishgypsies.co.uk

Innkeepers
- Liquor Licensing
  www.scan.org.uk/knowledgebase/topics/liquor_topic.htm

Perthshire
- Inns in the Carse of Gowrie 1806: return of hotels, inns and public
  houses, &c., in the Carse of Gowrie Licencing District on 29th April 1806
  www.genuki.org.uk/big/sct/PER/inns.html

Iron Founders
- My ancestor ... worked in the Ironfounding Industries
  **www.falkirk.gov.uk/services/community/cultural_services/
  museums/archives/iron_founding.pdf**

Lighthousemen

- National Archives of Scotland: Scottish Lighthouses
  www.nas.gov.uk/guides/lighthouses.asp
- Lighthouses
  www.scan.org.uk/knowledgebase/topics/lighthouses_topic.htm
- Lighthouse Records
  www.scan.org.uk/researchrtools/lighthouse.htm

Medical Professions

- UK Medical Registers, 1859-1959
  **http://search.ancestry.co.uk/iexec/?htx=List&dbid=
                  33538&offerid=0%3a7858%3a0**
  Including Scottish medics. Pay per view
- Royal College of Surgeons of Edinburgh Library & Special Collections
  www.library.rcsed.ac.uk/content/content.aspx
  Click 'historical enquiries' for information on family history research
- Library and Archives of the Royal College of Physicians and Surgeons of Glasgow
  **www.rcpsg.ac.uk/FellowsandMembers/libraryservices/
                          Pages/libraryservices.aspx**
  Click on 'Archive Collections' for a page on family history

Militia & Volunteers

Kincardineshire

- The Kincardineshire Volunteers
  http://myweb.tiscali.co.uk/nescotland/articles/militia1.htm
  Lists volunteers, 1798-1816

Kirkcudbrightshire

- An outline of the Urr Militia 1802, 1808
  http://donjaggi.net/galloway/urrmilitia.html

Perthshire

- Militia Collection PE66
  **www.pkc.gov.uk/Education+and+learning/Libraries
              +archives+and+learning+centres/Archives/Archive+
              collections/Online+sources/Militia+collections+PE66**
  Includes databases of 'Perthshire Militia Petitions, c1704-1859, mainly 1790-1810', 'Perthshire Militia Certifications, 1802-1810', and 'Assorted Perthshire Militia papers, 1680-1891, mainly 1785-1820'

Ross & Cromarty

- Annotated Transcriptions of Militia Lists
  http://freepages.genealogy.rootsweb.ancestry.com/~coigach/#census
  For Coigach, 1798-1827
- Cromarty Courthouse Museum: Militia List for the parish of Cromarty, 1814: all males in the parish aged between the ages of 17 and 45.
  www.cali.co.uk/users/freeway/courthouse/geneal1.html

Sutherland

- Clyne Militia List 1826
  www.countysutherland.co.uk/9.html
- County Sutherland: Durness Militia List 1809
  www.countysutherland.co.uk/42.html
- County Sutherland: Farr Militia List, December 1809
  www.countysutherland.co.uk/70.html
- County Sutherland: Parish of Golspie Militia List 1826
  www.countysutherland.co.uk/62.html
- County Sutherland: Kildonan 1809 Militia List
  www.countysutherland.co.uk/53.html
- County Sutherland: 1745 Militia List
  www.countysutherland.co.uk/40.html
  For parts of Loth parish
- County Sutherland: Loth and Kildonan Militia List 1826
  www.countysutherland.co.uk/47.html
- County Sutherland: 1809 Rogart Militia List
  www.countysutherland.co.uk/67.html
- County Sutherland: 1824 Rogart Militia List
  www.countysutherland.co.uk/69.html
- County Sutherland: Tongue Militia List 1809
  www.countysutherland.co.uk/35.html

Miners & Mine Owners, *etc.*

- National Archives of Scotland: Coal Mining Records
  www.nas.gov.uk/guides/coalmining.asp
- Scottish Mining Museum
  www.scottishminingmuseum.com/

- Coal Mining History Resource Centre
  www.cmhrc.co.uk/site/home
  Includes `The national database of mining deaths in Great Britain' / Ian Winstanley
- Working Bibliography of the History of Coal Miners and Coal Mining in Scotland
  www.ex.ac.uk/~RBurt/MinHistNet/Scotbib.html

Fife
- The Fife Miners
  www.users.zetnet.co.uk/mmartin/fifepits
  Include a 'memorial book' listing miners who died in accidents

Midlothian
- Edinburgh's Mining Industry in 1896: a list of coal mines
  www.ex.ac.uk/~RBurt/MinHistNet/1896-04.htm
  Lists managers

West Lothian
- Linlithgow's Mining Industry in 1896: a list of coal mines
  www.ex.ac.uk/~RBurt/MinHistNet/1896-09.htm
  Names managers

Municipal Officers

Angus
- A List of Baillies, Provosts & Lord Provosts of the Burgh of Dundee, Scotland
  www.monikie.org.uk/dundeebailliesandprovosts.htm

Midlothian
- Bailies (magistrates) & Town Treasurers of the Burgh of Musselburgh
  www.ancestor.abel.co.uk/inv/bailie.html

Nurses
- Nurses and Nursing Services: Civilian
  www.nationalarchives.gov.uk/catalogue/researchguidesindex.asp
  Scroll down & click on title. Also leaflets on `Nurses and Nursing Services' in the British Army, the Royal Navy, and the Royal Air Force

Patentees
- Scottish Genealogy Society Information Leaflet: Patents & Inventions
  www.scotsgenealogy.com
  Click `on-line information' and title

Patients
See also Medical Professions
- List of Patients, Smallpox Hospital, Mounthooly, Aberdeen
  www.scan.org.uk/researchrtools/medicalrecords.htm
  For 1872-5

Photographers
- Fife Photographers to 1900
  www.fifefhs.org/Records/photographers.htm

Pilots
- Pilots Returns for Aberdeen 1854-1910
  http://web.archive.org/web/20070327223710/ http://www.geocities. com/SoHo/Workshop/2299/pilots.html

Policemen
- My Ancestor was a policeman or policewoman
  www.scan.org.uk/familyhistory/myancestor/policeman.htm
- Policing and Police Forces
  www.scan.org.uk/knowledgebase/topics/policing_topic.htm
- Tracing Police Records
  www.scan.org.uk/knowledgebase/topics/police_tracingrecords.htm
- Police Records
  www.scan.org.uk/knowledgebase/topics/policerecords_topic.htm

Lanarkshire
- Police Archives
  www.glasgow.gov.uk/en/Residents/Library_Services/ The_Mitchell/Archives/policearchives.htm
  For Glasgow and the West of Scotland from the 1820s

Stirlingshire
- Falkirk Council Cultural Services Guide to Archives: Police Records
  **www.falkirk.gov.uk/services/community/cultural_services/
  museums/archives/finding_aids/PDFs/central_scotland_police.pdf**

Railwaymen
- National Archives of Scotland: Railway Records
  www.nas.gov.uk/guides/railway.asp
- Scotland, Highland Railway Company, January 1854 - 1900
  www.ancestry.co.uk/search/db.aspx?dbid=4959
  Pay per view

Royal Marines
- Royal Marines: Officers Service Records
  www.nationalarchives.gov.uk/catalogue/researchguidesindex.asp
  Scroll down & click on title. Also page on `Royal Marines: Other Ranks
  Service Records', *etc*.

Seamen (Merchant)
- Family Search Research Wiki: Scotland Merchant Marine
  https://wiki.familysearch.org/en/Scotland_Merchant_Marine
- Merchant Seamen: Records of the RGSS: A Guide to Leaflets
  www.nationalarchives.gov.uk/catalogue/researchguidesindex.asp
  Scroll down & click on title. Lists a variety of guides
- Scottish Maritime Records, 1600-1850 / David Dobson
  **http://search.ancestry.co.uk/iexec/?htx=BookList&dbid=
  49350&offerid=0%3a7858%3a0**
  Introduction to records, originally published Genealogical Publishing
  Co., 1999. Pay per view

Seamen (Royal Navy)
- Royal Navy: Officers Service Records
  www.nationalarchives.gov.uk/catalogue/researchguidesindex.asp
  Scroll down & click title. Also many other pages on Royal Navy records

Shipbuilders
- National Archives of Scotland: Shipbuilding Records
  www.nas.gov.uk/guides/shipbuilding.asp

Ship Owners & Masters
- Shipping Registers
  www.dgcommunity.net/historicalindexes/shipping.aspx
  For the ports of Dumfries 1824-1904, Kirkcudbright 1824-41, Stranraer,
  1824-1908, and Wigtown 1832-1920; includes names of ships' masters
  and owners

Shoemakers
- Burntisland Shoemakers 1685-1835
  www.fifefhs.org/Records/trades/burntshoe.htm

Soldiers
- British Army Lists
  www.nationalarchives.gov.uk/catalogue/researchguidesindex.asp
  Scroll down & click title. Also many other pages on the British Army
  and soldiers' records.
- British Military Records
  www.genuki.org.uk/big/BritMilRecs.html
- Family Search Research Wiki: Scotland Military Records
  https://wiki.familysearch.org/en/Scotland_Military_Records
- National Archives of Scotland: Military Records
  www.nas.gov.uk/guides/military.asp
- The Scots at War Trust
  www.scotsatwar.org.uk/
- United Kingdom and Ireland Military Records
  www.genuki.org.uk/big/MilitaryRecords.html
  Includes links to many National Archives leaflets
- Scottish Military History Website
  www.btinternet.com/~james.mckay/dispatch.htm
  www.btinternet.com/~james.mckay/yeoman04.htm
- The Black Watch Regimental Archive & Research
  www.theblackwatch.co.uk/index/regimental-archive-and-research

Angus
- Muster Rolls of Angus, Scotland: South African War 1899-1900
  www.monikie.org.uk/ah-musterroll.htm

Ayrshire

Ayrshire's Military History
www.genuki.org.uk/big/sct/AYR/military.html
Ayrshire Rifle Volunteers: Maybole Company Muster Roll
www.maybole.org/history/Archives/rifle/volunteers.htm
Late 19th c.

Fife

Loyal Tay Fencibles
www.fifefhs.org/loyaltay.htm
Various lists of men 1794-1801

Invernessshire

Soldiers discharged from the British Army who had given their
parish of birth as Urquhart, Inverness-shire.
http://freepages.genealogy.rootsweb.ancestry.com/~ked1/WO97.htm

Wigtownshire

- Wigtownshire Pages: Chelsea Royal Hospital: Discharged
  Soldier List
  http://freepages.history.rootsweb.ancestry.com/~leighann/
  county/intro_soldiers.html

Students

- My Ancestor was a University Student
  www.scan.org.uk/familyhistory/myancestor/student.htm
- Edinburgh University Archives guide 1: Student Records
  www.lib.ed.ac.uk/resources/collections/specdivision/euaguide1.shtml
- The University of Glasgow Story: University Alumni
  www.universitystory.gla.ac.uk/alumni/
  Includes database of graduates to 1896

Teachers

- My Ancestor was a Schoolteacher
  www.scan.org.uk/familyhistory/myancestor/schoolteacher.htm
- Corstorphine Schoolmasters 1646-1924
  www.angelfire.com/ct2/corstorphine/index7.html

- Corstorphine Teachers
  www.angelfire.com/ct2/corstorphine/index7a.html
  From the 1881 census

Textile Workers

- Scottish Textile Heritage
  www.scottishtextileheritage.org.uk

Theatrical Workers

- Scottish Theatre Archive
  http://special.lib.gla.ac.uk/sta

Witches

- The Survey of Scottish Witchcraft 1563-1736
  www.shc.ed.ac.uk/Research/witches
  Includes database of over 4,000 names
- Witchcraft in Scotland
  www.scan.org.uk/knowledgebase/topics/witchcraft.htm

13. Gazetteers and Maps

The family historian will frequently need to identify places mentioned in sources. Gazetteers and maps will have to be consulted. For an introduction to the use of Gazetteers, see:
- Family Search Research Wiki: Scotland Gazetteers
  https://wiki.familysearch.org/en/Scotland_Gazetteers

See also:
- Family Search Research Wiki: Scotland Historical Geography
  https://wiki.familysearch.org/en/Scotland_Historical_Geography

There are a number of web-based gazetteers. For a brief guide to them, see:
- United Kingdom and Ireland Gazetteers
  www.genuki.org.uk/big/Gazetteers.html

Gazetteers include:
- Pinpointing Locations
  www.scotlandspeople.gov.uk/content/help/index.aspx?r=551&564
- Gazetteer for Scotland
  www.geo.ed.ac.uk/scotgaz/gaztitle.htm
- The Gazetteer of Scotland 1882
  www.worldvitalrecords.com/indexinfo.aspx?ix=qcd52_scotlandgaz
  Pay per view database

- Gazetteer of Scottish Places
  www.scan.org.uk/knowledgebase/gazetteer/counties.htm
- Gazetteer of British Place Names
  www.gazetteer.co.uk
- Ordnance Gazetteer of Scotland / Francis H. Groome (ed.)
  www.electricscotland.com/history/gazetteer/index.htm
- Ordnance Gazetteer of Scotland
  www.ancestry.com/search/db.aspx?dbid=7292
  Pay per view database
- Ordnance Gazetteer of Scotland 1896
  www.worldvitalrecords.com/indexinfo.aspx?ix=qcd_549_scotlandgaz
  Pay per view database

- Ordnance Survey Placenames Gazetteer
  www.ordnancesurvey.co.uk/oswebsite/freefun/didyouknow
- Scotlands Places
  www.scotlandsplaces.gov.uk
  Combines gazetteer with detailed maps

The best published gazetteer has been digitised:
- A Topographical Dictionary of Scotland / Samuel Lewis
  www.british-history.ac.uk/source.aspx?pubid=308
  Vol.1 of this work is also available, pay per view, at
  www.worldvitalrecords.com/indexinfo.aspx?ix=qcd58_vol1

An awareness of the historic administrative divisions of Scotland is also important, since they may determine the location of sources. Consult:
- Administrative Areas of Scotland
  www.genuki.org.uk/big/Regions/Scotland.html

For a map of the historic Scottish counties, see:
- Scottish Counties before 1974
  www.rootsweb.com/~sctayr/counties.jpg

A list of Scottish counties and their parishes is provided at:
- Scottish Counties and their Parishes
  www.ancestor.abel.co.uk/county.html

There are many map sites on the internet. For a general introduction, see:
- Family Search Research Wikie: Scotland Maps
  https://wiki.familysearch.org/en/Scotland_Maps

Amongst the more useful map sites are:
- Genmaps: old and interesting maps of England Wales and Scotland
  http://freepages.genealogy.rootsweb.ancestry.com/
  ~genmaps/index.htm
- National Library of Scotland: Maps
  www.nls.uk/collections/maps
- Old Maps.co.uk
  www.old-maps.co.uk
  On-line Ordnance Survey maps

- Ordnance Gazetteer of Scotland: County Maps
  www.worldvitalrecords.com/indexinfo.aspx?ix=qcd549_maps
- Scotland: Maps (Ordnance Survey)
  www.british-history.ac.uk/place.aspx?gid=64&region=7
  Digitised versions of the original 1:2,500 & 1:10,560 Ordnance Survey maps
- Ordnance Survey Large Scale Scottish Town Plans, 1847-1895
  www.nls.uk/digitallibrary/map/townplans
- My Ancestor was an Islander
  www.scan.org.uk/familyhistory/myancestor/islander.htm

County Map Sites

Aberdeenshire
- Aberdeenshire Gazetteer of Place Names
  www.urie.demon.co.uk/genuki/ABD/_gazetteer/index.html
- Aberdeenshire Parish Map
  www.urie.demon.co.uk/genuki/ABD/parishmap1.html

Ayrshire
- Outline Parish Maps: Ayrshire
  www.genuki.org.uk/big/sct/AYR/ayrparish.html
- Ayrshire Parish Map
  www.genuki.org.uk/big/sct/AYR/ayr_pmap.html
- County of Ayrshire
  www.rootsweb.ancestry.com/~sctayr/ayr.jpg
  Parish map

Berwickshire
- Berwickshire Gazetteer
  www.genuki.org.uk/big/sct/BEW/gazetteer
- Berwickshire Maps
  www.genuki.org.uk/big/sct/BEW/mapList.html

Buteshire
- Buteshire Parish Map
  www.genuki.org.uk/big/sct/BUT/butpmap.html

Dumfriesshire
- Dumfriesshire Parish Map
  www.genuki.org.uk/big/sct/DFS/parish_map.html
- Locating and Researching Place-Names in Dumfries and Galloway
  www.dgfhs.org.uk/Ian-Anderson/index-2.htm

Dunbartonshire
- Dunbartonshire Parish Map
  www.genuki.org.uk/big/sct/DNB/dnbpmap.html

Fife
- Map and Parish Numbers of Fife & Kinross
  www.fifefhs.org/Maps/parishmap.htm
- Where in Fife?
  www.fifefhs.org/Maps/whereinfife.htm

Kincardineshire
- Kincardineshire Parish Map
  www.sol.co.uk/m/mmorton/genuki/KCD/parmap.htm

Kinrossshire
See Fife

Lanarkshire
- County of Lanark
  www.rootsweb.ancestry.com/~sctayr/lanark.jpg
  Parish map
- Glasgow's Renamed Streets
  www.douglasbrown.co.uk/stindex.html
  Lists streets which have been re-named

Orkney
- Map of Parishes in the Islands of Orkney and Shetland
  www.scotlandsfamily.com/parish-map-orkney.htm

Peeblesshire
- Peeblesshire Map
  www.genuki.org.uk/big/sct/PEE/map.html

Roxburghshire
- Roxburghshire Gazetteer
  www.genuki.org.uk/big/sct/ROX/gazetteer>
- Roxburghshire Maps
  www.genuki.org.uk/big/sct/ROX/mapList.html

Selkirkshire
- Selkirkshire Gazetteer
  www.genuki.org.uk/big/sct/SEL/gazetteer
- Selkirkshire Maps
  www.genuki.org.uk/big/sct/SEL/mapList.html
  List

Shetland
See Orkney

Wigtownshire
- The Wigtownshire Pages Map Help
  http://freepages.history.rootsweb.ancestry.com/~leighann/
  maphelp.html

14. Miscellaneous Sites

Adoptees
- National Archives of Scotland: Adoption Records
  www.nas.gov.uk/guides/adoptions.asp
- General Register Office for Scotland: Adoption in Scotland
  www.gro-scotland.gov.uk/regscot/adoption.html

Biographies
- Family Search Research Wiki: Scotland Biography
  https://wiki.familysearch.org/en/Scotland_Biography

Border Reivers
- In Search of the Border Reivers
  www.borderreivers.co.uk

Churches
- Genuki Church Database
  www.genuki.org.uk/big/parloc
- Scotland: Church History
  www.genuki.org.uk/big/sct/ChurchHistory.html

Fife
- Churches in Fife in the year 1893
  www.thefifepost.com/churches.htm

Clans
- COSCA: Council of Scottish Clans and Associations
  www.cosca.net
- Clans and Families of Ireland and Scotland: An Ethnography of
  the Gael A.D. 500 - 1750 / C. Thomas Cairney
  www.electricscotland.com/webclans/cairney/index.htm
- The Gathering of the Clans
  www.nessie.co.uk/clan/clanindx.html
- Genealogy Scotland: Clans; history
  http://members.tripod.com/~Caryl_Williams/scot.html
  Gateway

- Genealogists for the Scottish Clans
  http://thecapitalscot.com/scotgenealogy/clangenealogist.html

Country Houses
- The Country House Database: Scotland
  www.r-alston.co.uk/ch_sco.htm
  Lists country houses and the families who lived in them

Covenanters
- Covenanter
  http://en.wikipedia.org/wiki/Covenanter
- Scottish Covenanters Index
  www.ancestry.co.uk/search/db.aspx?dbid=7021
  Pay per view
- Scottish Covenanter Memorials Association
  www.covenanter.org.uk

Dates & Times
- Days, Dates, and Calendars
  www.scan.org.uk/knowledgebase/topics/daysanddates_topic.htm

Divorce
- National Archives of Scotland: Divorce and Separation Records
  www.nas.gov.uk/guides/divorce.asp

Emigration
There are numerous sites devoted to Scottish emigration. For introductory websites, see:
- National Archives of Scotland: Emigration
  www.nas.gov.uk/guides/emigration.asp
- Family Search Research Wiki: Scotland Emigration and Immigration
  https://wiki.familysearch.org/en/Scotland_Emigration_
  and_Immigration
- Emigration
  www.scan.org.uk/knowledgebase/topics/emigration_topic.htm
  Brief but authoritative

- My Ancestor was an Emigrant
  www.scan.org.uk/familyhistory/myancestor/emigrant.htm
- My Ancestor was Transported
  www.scan.org.uk/familyhistory/myancestor/transported.htm
- Emigration Records
  www.scan.org.uk/researchrtools
  Includes database of Highlands and Islands Emigration Society passenger lists 1852-1857
- National Library of Scotland: Scots Abroad
  www.nls.uk/catalogues/online/scotsabroad/index.html

A number of sites provide extensive gateways to the innumerable passenger list websites (which are far too numerous to list here):
- Immigrant Ships Transcribers Guild: Scottish Ports
  www.immigrantships.net
- Harold Ralston's Ancestor Ship passenger lists
  www.ralstongenealogy.com/shiplist.htm

A major new venture is currently being planned:
- Scottish Emigration Museum
  www.scottishemigrationmuseum.com

Over 21,000 passengers from Scotland, 1890-1960, are listed at:
- Scottish Emigration Database
  www.abdn.ac.uk/emigration

By County
Ayrshire
- Ayrshire born - foreign buried
  http://homepages.rootsweb.ancestry.com/~ayrshire/
  indexforeign.html
  Strays from burial records

Fife
- Fife, Scotland (E)migration Patterns Project
  www.rootsweb.com/~sctfif/ffemgr.html
  Contributed entries, with contributors email addresses

Invernessshire

See also Selkirkshire
- Hebridean Scots of the Province of Quebec / Peter MacDonald
  http://hebridscots.com
- Inverness Emigrant Index
  http://freepages.genealogy.rootsweb.ancestry.com/
                                    ~maddenps/INVEM1.htm

Orkney

- Orkneymen with the Hudsons Bay Company
  www.genuki.org.uk:8080/big/sct/OKI/canada.html

Perthshire

- Emigration from Perthshire to Canada in the early 19th century
  www.taybank.org.uk
  Click 'site search' and search 'emigration'

Selkirkshire

- Selkirk settlers identified from past and present of P.E.I., Skye and
  Hebridean Pioneers, and Other Sources: Passenger List Reconstruction
  for the *Dykes*, 1803
  www.islandregister.com/dykes.html
  Also includes reconstruction for the *Polly*, 1803

Sutherland

- County Sutherland Emigration Lists
  www.countysutherland.co.uk/44.html
  For Clyne, 1829-47
- County Sutherland: Emigrants from Dornoch
  www.countysutherland.co.uk/30.html
  For 1829-47
- County Sutherland: Emigrants from Golspie
  www.countysutherland.co.uk/37.html
  For 1829-47
- County Sutherland: Emigration from Lairg
  www.countysutherland.co.uk/29.html
  Early 19th c.
- County Sutherland: People who Emigrated
  www.countysutherland.co.uk/38.html
  From Loth & Kildonan, 1829-47
- County Sutherland: Emigrants from Rogart
  www.countysutherland.co.uk/45.html
  For 1829-47

By Overseas Destination

Australia

- Large Scale Emigration to Australia after 1845
  www.electricscotland.com/history/australia/scotaus3.htm
- Scots Down Under
  www.britannia.com/celtic/scotland/scot19.html
  Encyclopedia article
- Scots Australian History: the Scots who came to Australia
  www.electricscotland.com/history/australia/scotsin_australia.htm
- Born in the Border Counties of Scotland
  www.genuki.org.uk/big/sct/misc/strays.txt
  List of emigrants marrying in Victoria, Australia, 1853-95
- Australian (Victoria) immigrants from Lanarkshire
  www.scottap.com/family/Lanark/AusImmigrants.html

Canada

See also United States
- Electric Scotland: Canada
  www.electricscotland.com/canada/index.htm
- The Scots in Canada
  www.britannia.com/celtic/scotland/scot18.html
  Encyclopedia Article
- Scots in New Scotland (Nova Scotia), Canada
  www.chebucto.ns.ca/Heritage/FSCNS/ScotsHome.html
- Emigration Records from England and Scotland to Prince
  Edward Island
  www.islandregister.com/fhc/engscot.html
- Immigrants to Canada: Letters collected by the Canada Company
  to encourage emigration, 1842
  www.ist.uwaterloo.ca/~marj/genealogy/letters/1842letters.html

Orkneymen with the Hudson's Bay Company
www.genuki.org.uk/big/sct/OKI/canada.html
The Perth County Pioneers
http://my.tbaytel.net/bmartin/perth.htm
Emigration to Canada from Perthshire

Europe
Scots in Poland, Russia and the Baltic States, 1550-1850 / David Dobson
http://search.ancestry.co.uk/iexec/?htx=BookList&dbid= 49342&offerid=0%3a7858%3a0
Originally published Genealogical Publishing, 2003. Pay per view

New Zealand
- New Zealand: Scottish Historical Connections
www.electricscotland.com/history/nz/index.htm

South America
- Scots in Latin America / David Dobson
http://search.ancestry.co.uk/iexec/?htx=BookList&dbid= 49340&offer id=0%3a7858%3a0
Originally published Genealogical Publishing Co., 2003. Pay per view
The Scots in Argentina (including Argentine and Chilean Patagonia)
http://myweb.tiscali.co.uk/scotsinargpat/index.htm

United States
- A Dictionary of Scottish Emigrants to the U.S.A / Donald Whyte
www.worldvitalrecords.com/indexinfo.aspx?ix= gpc0806348178_donaldwhyte
Originally published 1972. Pay per view
- The Original Scots Colonists of Early America, 1612-1783
http://search.ancestry.co.uk/iexec/?htx=BookList&dbid= 48520&offerid=0%3a7858%3a0
Digitised version of a printed book. Pay per view
- Directory of Scots Banished to the American Plantations, 1650 - 1775 / David Dobson
www.worldvitalrecords.com/indexinfo.aspx?ix= gpc0806310359_directoryscots
Originally published 1983. Pay per view

- Directory of Scottish Settlers in North America, 1625-1825
http://search.ancestry.co.uk/iexec/?htx=BookList&dbid= 48523&offerid=0%3a7858%3a0
Digitised version of printed books. 6 further webpages. Pay per view
- Scots in the USA and Canada, 1825-1875 / David Dobson
http://search.ancestry.co.uk/iexec/?htx=BookList&dbid= 49343&offerid=0%3a7858%3a0
In 3 parts, on 2 further pages. Originally published Genealogical Publishing Co., 2001-4. Pay per view
- The Scots in the USA
http://britannia.com/celtic/scotland/scot17.html
Article
- Scots Emigration/Immigration to the U.S.
www.siliconglen.com/Scotland/11_24.html
- Scots in the USA and Canada, 1825-1875
http://search.ancestry.co.uk/iexec/?htx=BookList&dbid= 48532&offerid=0%3a7858%3a0
Digitised version of a printed book. Pay per view
- Scots on the Chesapeake
http://search.ancestry.co.uk/iexec/?htx=BookList&dbid= 48519&offerid=0%3a7858%3a0
Digitised version of a printed book. Pay per view
- Scots in the Mid-Atlantic Colonies, 1635-1783 / David Dobson
http://search.ancestry.co.uk/iexec/?htx=BookList&dbid= 49346&offerid=0%3a7858%3a0
Originally published Genealogical Publishing Co., 2002. Pay per view
- Scots in the Mid-Atlantic States, 1783-1883 / David Dobson
http://search.ancestry.co.uk/iexec/?htx=BookList&dbid= 49347&offerid=0%3a7858%3a0
Originally published Genealogical Publishing Co., 2002. Pay per view
- Directory of Scots in the Carolinas, 1680-1830
http://search.ancestry.co.uk/iexec/?htx=BookList&dbid= 48518&offerid=0%3a7858%3a0
Digitised version of a printed book. Pay per view
- Scotch-Irish Migration to South Carolina, 1772
http://search.ancestry.co.uk/iexec/?htx=BookList&dbid= 48628&offerid=0%3a7858%3a0
Digitised version of a printed book. Pay per view

- The Scottish Connection in Kansas
  http://skyways.lib.ks.us/genweb/republic/PatAdams/ScotIndex.html
  Includes links to surname pages

West Indies
- Scots in the West Indies, 1707-1857
  http://search.ancestry.co.uk/iexec/?htx=BookList&dbid=
  48533&offerid=0%3a7858%3a0
  Digitised version of a printed book. Pay per view

Events
- GENEVA: an Online Calendar of GENealogical EVents and Activities
  geneva.weald.org.uk
- Scottish Genealogy News & Events
  http://scottishancestry.blogspot.com/

Feudalism
- Farewell to Feudalism / Graham Senior-Milne
  www.scotsgenealogy.com
  Click 'on-line information' & title

Glossaries
- Glossary and Explanations
  www.scotsfind.org/glossary_access/glossary.pdf
- Research Tools: the Glossary
  www.scan.org.uk/researchrtools/glossary.htm
- Index of Legal Terms and Offences Libelled
  www.nas.gov.uk/guides/legalTerms.asp
- Wedderburn Pages: Glossary
  http://pagespro-orange.fr/euroleader/wedderburn/glossary.htm
- A Scots Glossary
  www.genuki.org.uk/big/sct/AYR/glossary.html
- Scottish Archive Network (SCAN) Glossary
  www.scan.org.uk/researchrtools/glossary.htm

Handwriting
See Palaeography

Heraldry
- Heraldry
  www.scan.org.uk/knowledgebase/topics/heraldry_topic.htm
- The Heraldry Society of Scotland: Scottish Heraldry Pages
  www.heraldry-scotland.co.uk/scotsherald.html
- A Note on Scottish Heraldry
  www.heraldica.org/topics/britain/scotland.htm
- An Annotated Bibliography of Scottish Heraldic Materials
  www.heraldica.org/topics/britain/scotbiblio.htm
- The Court of the Lord Lyon
  www.lyon-court.com
  The heraldic authority for Scotland
- Coats of Arms 1672-1909
  www.scotlandspeoplehub.gov.uk/research/
  coats-of-arms-1672-1908.htm
- General Armory of England, Scotland, Ireland and Wales / Sir Bernard Burke
  http://search.ancestry.co.uk/iexec/?htx=List&dbid=
  6326&offerid=0%3a7858%3a
  Originally published 1994. Pay per view
- An Ordinary of Scottish Arms / Sir James Balfour Paul
  www.worldvitalrecords.com/indexinfo.aspx?ix=
  gpc0806302739_ordinaryscottisharm
  Originally published 1903. Pay per view

Highland Clearances
- The Highland Clearances
  www.theclearances.org

Sutherland
- 1809 Golspie, Summons of Removal from the Sutherland Papers (SC9/7/58)
  www.countysutherland.co.uk/79.html

House History
- Researching the History of a House: a guide to archival sources / Grant E.L. Buttars
  www.fdca.org.uk/househistory.pdf
  Based on Dundee sources

- My Ancestor was a House Owner
  www.scan.org.uk/familyhistory/myancestor/houseowner.htm

Irish Immigration
- Scotch-Irish and Ulster Scot Research
  http://homepages.rootsweb.ancestry.com/~merle/
- Guide to Researching Irish Family/Social History in Dundee
  www.fdca.org.uk/FDCAIrishPage.html

Jacobites
- The Jacobite Risings 1715 and 1745
  www.nationalarchives.gov.uk/catalogue/researchguidesindex.asp
  Scroll down & click on title
- Jacobites of 1715 North East Scotland and Jacobites of 1745North East Scotland / Frances McDonnell
  http://search.ancestry.co.uk/iexec/?htx=BookList&dbid=49210&offerid=0%3a7858%3a0
  Originally published Genealogical Publishing Co,. 1998. Pay per view
- Jacobites of Lowland Scotland, England, Ireland, France, and Spain 1745 / Frances McDonnell
  http://search.ancestry.co.uk/iexec/?htx=BookList&dbid=49212&offerid=0%3a7858%3a0
  Originally published Genealogical Publishing Co., 2002. Pay per view

Angus
- The Jacobites of Angus, 1689-1746 / David Dobson
  http://search.ancestry.co.uk/iexec/?htx=BookList&dbid=49211&offerid=0%3a7858%3a0
  Originally published 2002. Pay per view

Kincardineshire
- Rebellion: Kincardineshire and the Rebellion of 1745-46
  http://myweb.tiscali.co.uk/nescotland/articles/rebs.htm
  List of rebels

Jews
- Scottish Jewish Archives Centre
  www.sjac.org.uk

- Jewish Genealogical Society of Great Britain: Scotland
  www.jgsgb.org.uk/sncscot.shtml

Journals
- Discover My Past Scotland
  http://scotland.discovermypast.co.uk/issue
  On-line journal

Local Government
- Scottish Local Government
  www.scan.org.uk/knowledgebase/topics/local_government_topic.htm
  Discussion of structure and records

Lookups
- Books We Own: Scotland
  www.rootsweb.ancestry.com/~bwo/scotland.html

Argyll
- Islay Virtual Library
  http://homepages.rootsweb.ancestry.com/~steve/islay/library.htm
  Look-ups offered

Dunbartonshire
- Volunteers and Look-ups
  www.rootsweb.com/~sctdnb/lookups.html
  Lookups offered for Dunbartonshire and Scotland in general

Missing People
- Lookup UK.com
  www.lookupuk.com/
  Site for finding missing people
- Salvation Army Family Tracing
  www2.salvationarmy.org.uk/en/Departments/familyTracing/Home.htm

Name Origins

- Family Search Research Wiki: Scotland Names Personal
  https://wiki.familysearch.org/en/Scotland_Names_Personal
- Scottish First Names
  www.namenerds.com/scottish
- Scottish Names Resources
  www.medievalscotland.org/scotnames
  Collection of articles on Scottish personal names
- Last Name Meanings: Thinking about Scottish Surnames /
  Sherry Irvine
  www.last-names.net/Articles/Scottish-Names.asp
- Surnames
  www.dwalker.pwp.blueyonder.co.uk/page127.htm
  Gives early locations and clans
- The Scottish Surnames of Colonial America / David Dobson
  http://search.ancestry.co.uk/iexec/?htx=BookList&dbid=
  49349&offerid=0%3a7858%3a0
  Originally published Genealogical Publishing Co., 2003. Pay per view

Aberdeenshire

- Aberdeenshire Personal Names
  www.urie.demon.co.uk/genuki/ABD/names.html
  Discussion of naming practices

Orphanages

- Quarriers
  www.quarriers.org.uk/helpline.php
  Children's home. Click 'Genealogy' for information on records
- The Golden Bride: Child Migration from Scotland to Canada, 1869-1939
  www.iriss.ac.uk/goldenbridge

Palaeography & Latin

- Family Search Research Wiki: Scotland Handwriting
  https://wiki.familysearch.org/en/Scotland_Handwriting
- Family Search Research Wiki: Latin Genealogical Word List
  https://wiki.familysearch.org/en/Latin_Genealogical_Word_List

- Scotlands People: Handwriting Help
  www.scotlandspeople.gov.uk/content/help/index.aspx?r=551&420
  Click below `handwriting guide'.
- Scottish Handwriting
  www.scottishhandwriting.com

Pedigrees

- United Kingdom and Ireland Records
  http://userdb.rootsweb.ancestry.com/uki
  Search records for c.250,000 individuals

Aberdeenshire

- From Aberdeenshire to the Ends of the Earth
  www.loadsofpeople.co.uk/

Ayrshire

- Ayrshire: Surnames Index Database
  www.ayrshire-roots.com/surnames.php

Berwickshire

- Borders Family History Society Family Tree Search
  www.bordersfhs.org.uk/BFHSFamilyTreeSearchForm.asp
  Collection of pedigrees from Berwickshire, Roxburghshire,
  Peeblesshire & Selkirkshire

Peebleshire
See Berwickshire

Roxburghshire
See Berwickshire

Selkirkshire
See Berwickshire

Peerage, *etc.*

- Burke's Peerage and Gentry: Scotland Articles & Resources
  www.burkespeerage.com/articles/scot-index.aspx

Peerage of Scotland and Ireland
**http://search.ancestry.co.uk/iexec/?htx=List&dbid=
7443&offerid=0%3a7858%3a0**
Originally published as vol.2 of Debrett, John. *The Peerage of England, Scotland, and Ireland*. 1808. Pay per view
- Peerage of the United Kingdom and Ireland, Volumes I-IV / George Edward Cockayne
**http://search.ancestry.co.uk/iexec/?htx=List&dbid=
6717&offerid=0%3a7858%3a0**
Originally published 1910-16. Pay per view
- Family Search Research Wiki: Scotland Nobility
https://wiki.familysearch.org/en/Scotland_Nobility

Royalty
- Scotland Royal Genealogy
www.scotlandroyalty.org
- The Scottish Monarchy
www.highlanderweb.co.uk/monarch1.htm

Surname Variants
- Scottish Surnames and Variants
www.scotlandspeople.gov.uk/content/help/index.aspx?560
- A List of Scottish Surname Variants
www.scotsfind.org/surnames_access/surnames.pdf
- Name Thesaurus
www.imagepartners.co.uk/Welcome.aspx

Tartans
- Tartans of Scotland
www.tartans.scotland.net

Weights & Measures
- Scottish Genealogy Society Information Leaflet: Scottish Weights & Measures
www.scotsgenealogy.com
Click `on-line information' & title

15. Professional Services, Booksellers *etc.*

A. Professional Genealogists
The websites of professional genealogists are not listed here. If you do want to employ a professional to undertake research, you should first visit:
- Association of Scottish Genealogists and Record Agents
www.asgra.co.uk

See also:
- Genealogy Pro: Scotland & Scottish Genealogy
http://genealogypro.com/directories/Scotland.html
Commercial list of researchers

For professional researchers willing to undertake work at the National Archives in London, consult:
- Independent Researchers
www.nationalarchives.gov.uk/irlist

B. Other Services
- Abeshaus
www.abeshaus.com/new/Genealogy/scottish.htm
American bookshop
- Archive CD Books
www.archivecdbooks.org
CD's
- The Best Books on Scotland
www.scotland-inverness.co.uk/scotbks.htm
Bookseller
- Scottish Genealogical Research Consultant and Emigration Specialist: David Dobson, MPhil (St Andrews) PhD (Aberdeen)
www.btinternet.com/~lds.dobson
Professional genealogist's page, but included here for the extensive listing of Dobson's books for the Scottish family historian
- Genealogical Publishing Co: Scotland/Scottish
www.genealogical.com/countries/Scotland/Scottish.html

- Graham Maxwell Ancestry: Bookshop
  www.maxwellancestry.com/ancestry/publishing/publishing.htm
  Publishers of census and other transcripts
- S & N Genealogy Supplies
  www.genealogysupplies.co.uk
  Publishers of CD's
- SG Transcriptions
  www.sgtranscriptions.co.uk
  Publishers of death register transcripts *etc.,* for Berwickshire, Peeblesshire, Roxburghshire & Selkirkshire

Subject Index

Institution & Author Index

Place Index